Southern Hemisphere of the Moon

(SEE INDEX OVERLEAF)

INDEX TO MAP OF THE MOON

MAN AND THE MOON, Robert S. Richardson
and Chesley Bonestell.

"Space exploration of the moon is presented
in this compilation of articles by Wilkins,
Von Braun, Clark, Whipple and others. Interesting journey for space armchair
travelers."--LIBRARY JOURNAL

"For moon-travelers in their rocking-chairs,
here is an amusing and informative guide,
for successful exploration of our satellite."
THE NEW YORK TIMES

"A large and lavish book about the moon
which includes everything from descriptions
of various features of the moon by modern
astronomers (up to the Russians' account of
the moon's other side), to details of how
man will get to the moon and what he will do
there -- by such writers as Arthur C. Clarke,
Wernher von Braun, and Fred Whipple."
ENGINEERING AND SCIENCE

"A whale of a book for the youth today."
THE CHRISTIAN HERALD

MAN

CLEVELAND AND NEW YORK

AND THE MOON

COMMENTARY BY *Robert S. Richardson*

ILLUSTRATIONS BY *Chesley Bonestell*

THE WORLD PUBLISHING COMPANY

Published by *The World Publishing Company*
2231 West 110th Street, Cleveland 2, Ohio

Published simultaneously in Canada by
Nelson, Foster & Scott Ltd.

Library of Congress Catalog Card Number: 61-5813

FIRST EDITION

Acknowledgment is made to the following for selections used in this book:

For "The Explorers" by Adrienne Rich. Copyright © 1953 by The New Yorker Magazine, Inc.

For "The Formation of the Craters" and "Astronomical Observations from the Moon," reprinted from *Exploring Mars* by Robert S. Richardson by permission of McGraw-Hill Book Company, Inc. Copyright 1954 by Robert S. Richardson.

For "The Circular Maria," reprinted from *The Face of the Moon* by Ralph B. Baldwin by permisson of The University of Chicago Press. Copyright 1949.

For "The Earth-Moon Journey," reprinted from *Interplanetary Flight* by Arthur C. Clarke by permission of the author, Temple Press, Ltd., and Scott Meredith Literary Agency, Inc.

HC461

The Explorers

A D R I E N N E   R I C H

Beside the Mare Crisium, that sea
Where water never was, sit down with me
And let us talk of Earth, where long ago
We drank the air and saw the rivers flow
Like comets through the green estates of man,
And fruit the color of Aldebaran
Weighted the curving boughs. The route of stars
Was our diversion, and the fate of Mars
Our grave concern; we stared throughout the night
On these uncolonized demesnes of light.
We read of stars escaping Newton's chain
Till only autographs of fire remain.
We aimed our mortal searchlights into space
As if in hopes to find a mortal face.

O little Earth, our village, where the day
Seemed all too brief, and starlight would not stay,
We were provincials on the grand express
That whirled us into dark and loneliness.
We thought to bring you wonder with a tale
Huger than those that turned our fathers pale.
Here in this lunar night, we watch alone
Longer than ever men have watched for dawn.
Beyond this meteor-bitten plain we see
More starry systems than you dream to be,
And while their clockwork blazes overhead
We speak the names we learned as we were bred;
We tell of places seen each day from birth—
Obscure and local, patios of the Earth!
O race of farmers, plowing year by year
The same few fields, I sometimes seem to hear
The far-off echo of a cattle bell
Against the cratered cliff of Arzachel,
And weep to think no sound can ever come
Across that outer desert from my home!

Contents

CONTENTS

Illustrations

(Since an astronomical telescope gives an inverted image, all maps and photographs in this book, unless otherwise indicated, are printed with South at the top. These illustrations appear following page 96.)

ILLUSTRATIONS

* Introduction

There is no doubt about it. The most neglected body in the sky is the moon. Visitors to an observatory are always amazed to hear that astronomers seldom bother to look at the moon. They can't understand it. They think astronomers spend most of their time looking at the moon. The truth of the matter is that about the only time astronomers at a large observatory ever bother to turn their telescopes on the moon is when a V.I.P. comes around who has to be shown some spectacular object. Astronomers don't even like the moon very well. To most of them it is a totally useless object up there in the sky that stops them from working half the month. Astronomers use their telescopes mostly as huge cameras for photographing celestial objects. They put a sensitive plate at the focus of their telescope and expose it to the sky. These exposures may last for minutes or hours. But suppose the sky is filled with moonlight. Then the plate will be fogged and the photograph ruined. Hence it is impossible to do direct photography when the moon is in the sky.

At first glance, the moon seems like an exciting object, especially if one examines it at the quarter phase when the various formations are thrown into strong relief by the black shadows. It is fascinating to let the eye wander over the surface picking out objects of interest. Here is a crater whose rim is just coming into illumination as a thin semicircle of light. Its floor is still buried in shadow. Or perhaps the shadow of the rim falls across the crater floor in a long jagged silhouette. Far over on the night side the tip of a peak catches the rays of the rising sun, standing out like a star against the blackness around it. In the southern hemisphere the craters are strewn so thickly they form a crazy pattern like a maze without beginning or end. One is reminded of the icing on a cake that has been violently agitated, then suddenly frozen into immobility. Viewed from a quarter of a million miles it doesn't seem quite real. Yet if we could bridge that gap we would find those mountains and craters are very real indeed. You could walk over them and touch them and scoop up a handful of the surface dust. And as it trickled through your fingers you could say to yourself, "This is not the old familiar earth any more. This is the moon. The lifeless sterile surface of the moon."

But there comes a time when the view begins to pall. Except for the shifting illumination of the sun's rays, nothing ever changes on the moon. Or if there are changes, as some insist, they are of a very minor sort. You can look at the moon tonight, tomorrow night, or a dozen years from now, and find exactly the same formations awaiting your scrutiny. There is plenty of material for detailed study but it is always the same detail. As a consequence, most astronomers turn to more rewarding objects for investigation in the sun, stars, and nebulae. From these bodies a whole spectrum of rays is launched into space which can give us a vast amount of information if only we can interpret the messages we receive. And there is an endless variety of changing objects for study—flare stars, pulsating stars, even exploding stars. By comparison, what has the moon to offer? A parade of the same identical features month after month. No wonder the moon has attracted so few devotees.

The study of the moon, in fact, belongs more properly in the realm of geochemistry or geophysics than astronomy. Very few astronomers are really qualified to make an intelligent study of the lunar surface. The few who have concentrated on selenology have found themselves isolated, with no one to talk to, out of the major trend of interest of the profession. This situation became so acute that a paper was published entitled *Is Selenology Extinct?*

But recently, interest in the moon has undergone a dramatic revival. The thought that we may actually live to see men on the moon has brought a sudden change in attitude toward our satellite. From being an object of casual inspection, the moon is coming to be regarded in somewhat the same way as a piece of property being considered for a homesite. After all, sending men to the moon is an expensive proposition. We would like to know some of the risks involved, as well as what we may expect for our money. The surprising fact that has emerged—which was no surprise at all to those familiar with the situation— is that reliable information on the moon is remarkably scarce.

One reason it is difficult to obtain information on the moon is that the literature on the subject is so widely scattered. When an astronomer wants to get information about the stars and nebulae, he knows exactly where to go. He consults the bound volumes of such scientific periodicals as the *Astrophysical Journal* or the *Monthly Notices of the Royal Astronomical Society* and a few others. But there is no particular place to look for papers written about the moon. They are scattered through dozens of diverse publications.

Once found, the papers describing the various lunar formations are all right for the expert who is devoted to their detailed study by telescope or photograph. Unfortunately, such papers which comprise the bulk of the literature on the moon are of scant interest to the general reader. One soon tires of enumerations of the various characteristics of the lunar features. And when it comes to the origin of the lunar features little progress is possible until more information can be obtained from on-the-spot observations.

This volume is concerned not only with the moon as an astronomical body, but also with the moon as it relates to man—from the time of Lucian's flight of fancy, to the matter-of-fact remarks of a mining engineer debating the best method of extracting oxygen from the lunar rocks. Until recently any discussion of man on the moon was of necessity considered pure fancy or at best regarded with amused tolerance. Now for the first time, travel to the moon seems actually within our grasp. We are not playing make believe any more. We are deadly serious. Every scrap of information we have pertaining to the moon may be of value. In particular, we need creative imagination in devising ways of turning the lunar desert to our purpose. For it is not enough merely to pay a flying visit to the moon and return. This will be a terrific task but it is only the start. To reap the full benefit of our labors we must establish a base on the moon that is entirely self-sufficient, one that is completely independent of the earth for the necessities of life and transportation. Only then can we say that we have really conquered space. Whether this will come about in the idealistic way some have envisaged, only time will tell. At any rate, it is with such problems that the papers in this book are mostly concerned, the realistic problems of man in relation to his nearest neighbor in space—the moon.

IMAGINARY VOYAGES TO

THE MOON

*

It may seem out of place in a book that deals with the moon in a highly realistic manner, to waste time on fictitious and often fantastic voyages to the moon. Yet I think it would be a mistake to brush aside these early flights to the moon and concentrate exclusively upon modern developments. For without a knowledge of this early material we have no perspective on the subject. Today the launching of a new artificial satellite is a matter of almost monthly occurrence. It scarcely makes the front page any more. But consider the plight of an author two hundred years ago who wanted to send some characters to the moon. In the entire history of the world, nobody had gotten farther off the ground than they could jump. (The first manned balloon flight was not until 1783.) How then was he going to get them all the way to the moon? His only recourse was to the few objects familiar to him that could rise above the ground, such as birds and clouds. It is not surprising therefore that in the first moon voyages, such as Lucian's, not much stress was laid on the method of transportation. The stories in fact were often written as social satires. As time went on, however, and authors became more scientifically minded, they tried to devise more plausible methods of getting their characters into space. These methods, if not scientifically sound, were often highly ingenious. We may scoff at them today or regard them with amused tolerance, yet for all their shortcomings they served to keep alive the idea of going to the moon. In the face of the most discouraging odds, the idea has displayed a remarkable persistence; it is a dream that has never completely died.

A story of a trip to the moon is a fairly good index of the popular attitude toward the moon and space travel at the time it was written. Most authors contemplating such a story have done considerable thinking on the subject beforehand, and have often consulted the current astronomical literature. Thus these fictitious flights, fanciful as they were, served to indicate the current state of selenology as well as the space-mindedness of the population. Our present conviction that we will ultimately reach the moon is, in fact, a comparatively recent development. From personal experience I know that previous to the launching of the first artificial satellite, the assertion that we might someday send a manned rocket to the moon was received with polite skepticism or shrugged off entirely. Now the pendulum has swung the other way. We are in a frame of mind to accept practically anything about interplanetary travel, regardless of whether the traffic is headed outward or toward us. Descriptions of trips to the moon and Mars have recently been written in such a realistic style and with so much minute attention to detail that we are apt to forget that they are still entirely fictitious. We are still probably many years away from manned interplanetary travel. When the big day finally does come, the instrumentation and methods employed may be so different from those envisaged now as to make them seem quite old-fashioned. The scientific fiction of one era is outdated by the technology of the next.

So far as we know, the first account of a journey to the moon was a gently spoofing yarn, the *True History*. It was written about 150 A.D. by a Syrian rhetorician, Lucian of Samosata. His story indicates that the people of his day already regarded the moon as another world not so different from their own. The idea that the planets are worlds and not mere points of light like the stars, was not scientifically accepted until about 1670—sixty years after the invention of the telescope—when markings were first sighted on the disk of Mars.

Even in Lucian's day it was known that the moon was not near. Two centuries earlier the great Hipparchus by a clever use of eclipse observations had reckoned the distance of the moon as fifty-nine radii of the earth, a value in remarkably close agreement with modern results. The size of the earth had also been measured in 250 B.C. by Eratosthenes of Alexandria. Hence the distance to the moon was no mystery to the ancients. If Lucian had ever heard of this work of Hipparchus and Eratosthenes there is no evidence of it from his stories. Lucian's attitude toward the moon seems to have been somewhat like that of Edgar Rice Burroughs of Tarzan fame in his novels such as *A Princess of Mars* and *The Warlord of Mars*—the less he knew about Mars the less he would be restricted to fact in writing about it. Whereas later writers went to great pains to devise a plausible method of transporting their characters to the moon, Lucian did it by the simple process of having a ship picked up in a whirlwind and deposited on the moon eight days later, accomplishing the whole trick in just two sentences. Doubtless this feat seemed reasonable enough to Lucian. We must remember that in his day people were completely ignorant of the extent of the atmosphere. They knew it extended to the tops of the highest mountains. There was no reason to suppose that it stopped there or that it did not continue indefinitely as far as the moon.

Of course, Lucian never intended that his story should be taken seriously. He was not trying to deceive people into thinking they were reading an actual account of a trip to the moon, as Poe later deceived people into thinking the Atlantic had been crossed when he wrote "The Balloon Hoax." Lucian is quite frank with his readers on this point, for he begins by remarking that he has no other intention in writing than to amuse. In fact, it is his avowed intention to tell all kinds of lies in the most plausible manner possible—a parody on certain poets and historians of old who had written "the truth" on subjects which quite obviously were entirely unknown to them. Lucian promises to keep good faith with his readers by admitting right at the start that his stories are outright lies.

Lucian and his party have hardly landed on the moon when they are met by some "Vulture Dragoons," who promptly put them under arrest and take them before their leader. This business of hailing new arrivals on a planet before the king is still standard procedure in many stories; basic situations in science fiction have not changed essentially in the last two thousand years. Considerable space is taken up in describing the inhabitants of the moon, who seem to be similar to various earth creatures enlarged many times. It seems strange, however, that Lucian nowhere mentions the appearance of the lunar surface itself. We would suppose that he might invent a few wonders for our edification, but in this regard he is completely silent. Lucian's chief interest was obviously in people and human relationships. There is not a shred of evidence in the *True History* that he had the slightest interest in natural science.

The story is also almost completely lacking in gadgetry. Surrounded as we are today by a wilderness of gadgets, it is hard for us to realize how barren the ancient world was of all mechanical contrivances except those of the simplest sort. Lucian does, however, introduce one gadget in his story. This is a well (not very deep) with a looking glass over it. At the bottom of this well you can hear everything that is said on earth. By looking into the mirror you can see every city and country on earth as plainly as if you were standing directly over them. Lucian does not elaborate on this contraption. He does not introduce plausible detail as Poe or Jules Verne would have done. You have to take the well and mirror just as they are without embellishment. Lucian insists they are there. If you don't believe it you can go to the moon and see for yourself.

After Lucian, however, travel to the moon languished for some fifteen hundred years. This is not surprising, for astronomy too languished during this period. Not until the invention of the telescope about 1609 was a new interest in the heavens generally aroused. Even a small telescope will reveal the mountains and craters on the moon and these findings evidently stimulated interest in our satellite. Shortly afterward several tales appeared dealing with voyages to the moon, but the transportation problem was still as formidable as ever. The increased knowledge of the heavens had as yet yielded no new principles that would successfully launch a man into space.

One of the first accounts of a flight to the moon to appear after the invention of the telescope was the *Somnium* of Johann Kepler. Kepler seems to have worked at it off and on for many years, but the book was finally printed in 1634. The *Somnium* is of special interest in that it was not written by a layman but by a professional astronomer, one of the greatest of all time. For it was Kepler who discovered the three fundamental laws of planetary motion as a result of a tremendous amount of figuring which would easily have discouraged a less determined man. The discovery of these three laws alone was enough to ensure

Kepler of a permanent place in astronomy.

It is unfortunate for Kepler's reputation as a scientist that he did not limit himself to discovering his three laws of planetary motion. For he also indulged in many other activities that must have seemed nonsensical even to scientists of his own time. To mention only a few, he cast horoscopes, made prophecies about the weather, and warned against the malign influence of comets. After reading some of his books one cannot help but wonder if he did not discover his three laws of planetary motion by trying a thousand and one schemes until he chanced upon some that worked. Yet there is an old saying that accidents have a way of happening to genius. It is unfair to minimize the credit that rightfully belongs to Kepler.

Kepler evaded the problem of how to get to the moon in somewhat the same way that we skirt the problem of how to eat corn on the cob at a formal dinner —we simply don't serve corn on the cob. Kepler did not even send his own physical body hurtling across space. He simply *dreamed* that he went to the moon, being carried there and back by demons who were able to operate in the void between the two worlds during eclipses when their shadows extended from one to the other.

By the seventeenth century, however, men had learned something about the surface of the moon, and this Kepler incorporates in his story. With his mystic temperament, he had no difficulty in supplying the moon with inhabitants. He describes them as snakelike creatures with faculties similar to our own. Kepler also gives one of the first explanations of the origin of the lunar craters. They are not due to natural causes but are constructed by the Endymionides, as he calls the inhabitants of the moon, for protection against their enemies as well as the heat of the sun. In the center of a chosen site, they set up a pole to which is attached a long rope; keeping the rope taut, they walk around the pole tracing out the edge of the crater as they go; then they proceed to build the wall of the crater along the line thus marked out. Kepler relates that "whenever the inhabitants feel annoyed by the power of the sun those who live near the center move into the shadow of the outer wall . . . following the shadow for fifteen days, they wander about and by this means endure the heat." It is hard to understand how the Endymionides would get much relief from the sun in this way, as the crater walls would cast little shadow near lunar noon when the temperature was highest. But as Kepler also remarked, there were numerous caves in the crater walls in which the inhabitants could take refuge when things got too hot.

Kepler's story suggests no new method of space travel and the reader feels decidedly cheated when he comes to the end and finds the whole thing is a dream. There are, however, a few compensations. Kepler surmises that we might run out of air on our way to the moon—a happy guess on his part. He ascribes magnetic forces to the moon and earth, so that when one is close enough to the moon, its magnetism predominates over that of the earth, causing a person to fall the rest of the way to the moon without further assistance from the demons. In ascribing an attractive force to the planets, some writers have claimed that Kepler anticipated the law of gravitation. It is quite certain, however, that Kepler had no notion of gravitational attraction as it was formulated half a century later by Newton.

Another moon book, which actually appeared in print a few years before the *Somnium,* was *Man in the Moone* (1638) by Bishop Francis Godwin. This has the distinction of being the first account of a trip to the moon written in English. Otherwise it is of no special interest in the history of lunar flight. The hero, Domingo Gonzales, trains some wild swans to carry weights and obey his orders. Eventually, he constructs a raft on which he can be carried aloft by the swans. He starts out on a journey one day without any intention of going to the moon. Imagine his dismay when he finds the swans heading straight for the moon as if they were used to migrating there, flying with a speed which he estimates at 175 miles an hour. They complete the journey in twelve days which would make the distance of the moon only 50,000 miles. The moon turns out to be an idyllic place inhabited by creatures who are human but much larger than earth men. In writing a moon story, Bishop Godwin does not seem to have been motivated either by science or satire. Apparently all he wanted to do was to write a romance—a story of marvelous events in faraway places. He seems to have been eminently successful.

The next story of a trip to the moon worth mentioning is Cyrano de Bergerac's *L'Autre Monde; ou, Les Estats et Empires de la Lune,* published in 1657. Cyrano was the famous swordsman with the long nose later immortalized in the play by Edmond Rostand. His story is notable for the ingenuity he displayed in getting his hero to the moon. He had noticed in the morning how dew is drawn upward by the rays of the sun. Why not apply the same method in getting a man to the moon? So his hero fastens vials of water around his waist and is carried aloft as the liquid is sucked upward by the sun. In later stories he used more elaborate devices. One was an iron car lifted by throwing a lodestone in front of it. The other was a box with rockets attached to it—the first mention of rocketry in space travel. It is certain, however, that Cyrano had no knowledge of action and reaction as exemplified by propulsive forces and it was not until 1686 that the principle involved was clearly stated by Newton.

Other stories of trips to the moon followed and although they contain some features of interest they never attained notoriety. In fact, we have to wait until the nineteenth century before we find a story of a trip to the moon which is still readily available. This is "The Unparalleled Adventures of One Hans Pfaal" by Edgar Allan Poe published in 1835 in the *Southern Literary Messenger.* The story is distinguished by the minute attention to detail so characteristic of Poe which gives the whole fantastic proceeding an air of reality and scientific authenticity. "Hans Pfaal" is unique among Poe's stories in that it contains some passages which may be called humorous. Humor was Poe's greatest failure. Nevertheless, the whole motive of Hans Pfaal in desiring to go to the moon has a certain grim humor about it. He did not want to go to the moon because it was a grand adventure or for scientific purposes. He wanted to go to the moon to escape from his creditors! Nowhere in the history of lunar flight do we find anyone with such a good and sufficient reason for wanting to depart this earth.

As a youngster residing in the family of John Allan, a wealthy merchant, Poe had had a telescope at his disposal large enough to reveal the more prominent lunar features distinctly. He had a keen interest in science and kept up with the latest developments of his day, as evidenced in "The Thousand-and-Second Tale of Scheherazade." Poe was also penniless most of his life and doubtless harassed by creditors. Hence it is not surprising that he thought longingly of escape from the manifold perplexities of this earth to the Lethean peace of the skies.

It required a prodigious amount of invention on Poe's part to keep the story of Hans Pfaal going for eighteen thousand words, for there is really not much that happens in it. It is told in the first person by Hans Pfaal himself, who relates his intolerable predicament with his creditors, and the necessity of escaping from them. For a while he contemplates suicide. Then it occurs to him that by going to the moon he can quit this earth just as effectively. Henceforth all his energy is bent upon reaching the moon.

When "Hans Pfaal" was written more than a century ago the balloon was still the only means by which man had succeeded in rising above the surface of the earth. Therefore, the balloon naturally suggested itself as a means of space travel. Furthermore, the balloon is a relatively uncomplicated device. Many flights had been made simply by inflating a bag with hot air. Poe did better: he has Hans Pfaal use a mysterious gas whose principal constituent is azote (an old name for nitrogen), which has a density 37.4 times less than that of hydrogen. The manufacture of the balloon and the gas to inflate it is all described in great detail. On the night of the take-off, three of Hans Pfaal's most annoying creditors help him, placated by the promise that they soon will be repaid. Having concealed some canisters of gunpowder near-by, Pfaal secretly ignites the fuse, with the result that he is only a few feet above ground when there is a tremendous explosion in which fire, gravel, and blazing metal are mixed with mangled limbs. Thus Hans Pfaal gets safely away while finishing off his creditors.

Poe evidently went to considerable trouble to look up data on the moon, for he gives accurate values for its size, mean distance, and the eccentricity of its orbit. He tries to make the distance between the earth and moon as small as possible by giving the distance between their surfaces instead of their centers, thus reducing the distance by 5,000 miles. Curiously enough, he does not give the distance of the moon when it is nearest the earth at the perigee of its orbit. By aiming for perigee he would have reduced the moon's distance by 13,000 miles, and Poe does use the word perigee so there is no doubt he was familiar with it. The inference is strong that Poe did not know how to calculate this distance.

What to do about providing his hero with air en route to the moon must have caused Poe considerable trouble. He skirts the difficulty by raising the question of whether we ever completely run out of air as we venture upward, and cites the results of measures of barometic pressure made on high mountain tops and balloon flights. Apparently no matter how high you go, there is always *some* air available. Even far out in space there is evidence of a thin atmosphere as shown by the acceleration of Encke's comet. These are pretty thin arguments today but in 1835 they doubtless sounded much more convincing. Poe therefore allowed Hans Pfaal a little atmosphere on his way to the moon, enough so that with the aid of an air pump which he operated by hand he was able to breathe without undue hardship.

Once Poe had accomplished his purpose and gotten his hero to the moon, he winds up the story abruptly just where you might logically expect it to begin. He tosses off a few casual remarks about the Selenites: they are small fat people with long crooked noses who seem to bear a striking resemblance to the seven dwarfs in *Snow White*. There is also an "incomprehensible connection between each particular individual on the moon with some particular individual on the earth . . . by means of which the lives and destinies of the inhabitants of the one are interwoven with the lives and destinies of the other." He also hints ominously at the "dark and hideous mysteries" which lie on the invisible side of the moon but he does not elaborate.

We discover that Hans Pfaal has an excellent reason for not revealing all he knows about the moon. After five years residence on its surface he pines for his home and family. But first there is that little matter of blowing up his three creditors which must be settled. He has no desire to return to earth only to be cast promptly into prison and hanged. So he has sent a Selenite back to earth in a balloon bearing an account of his trip to the moon, and requesting pardon for his crime. In exchange for a pardon he will give astronomers a detailed description of conditions on the moon, information of priceless value which they never could hope to obtain by looking through their telescopes. Unfortunately, the Selenite becomes terrified at the sight of the earth men and after delivering his message hurries away without obtaining an answer. And so presumably Hans Pfaal had to drag out the rest of his days upon our satellite. It is unfortunate that Poe never did relate Hans Pfaal's adventures on the moon. Had he done so he would have written the first piece of modern science fiction, and thus scooped the field, as he did with C. Auguste Dupin in the scientific detective story.

"The Unparalleled Adventures of One Hans Pfaal" is generally regarded as one of Poe's lesser stories. It contributes little of importance about going to the moon and says nothing about the moon itself. It does, however, set a new standard for verisimilitude. Poe labored mightily to give every incident an air of reality that is hard to resist. We can easily imagine that a gullible reader picking up the *Southern Literary Messenger* in 1835 might have been half convinced that Hans Pfaal actually did reach the moon. Thenceforth, any author who tackled the moon story could not get by with unscientific writing if he expected people to believe him.

Some thirty years passed before another author turned his eyes on the moon again. In 1864, a book was published entitled simply *Voyage to the Moon*, written by Chrysostom Trueman, a British clergyman. The voyage was made by using a mineral-repellant antigravity device which, as we shall see, was to crop up again about the turn of the century. A unique feature of this story was a live garden, taken along to replenish the air with oxygen; this clearly foreshadows the modern idea of using algae for this purpose. For some reason, the story was never popular and is practically unknown today. Perhaps it was a matter of timing, for only a year later an author who had already achieved a widespread reputation brought forth a new moon story. This was Jules Verne's *From the Earth to the Moon,* followed five years later in 1870 with a sequel, *Round the Moon.* Despite all the fictitious voyages to the moon that appeared later, this is still probably the most famous story of its kind ever written.

It is safe to say that *From the Earth to the Moon* was the first story in which the characters are sent to the moon by a method remotely capable of getting them there. The setting is Baltimore shortly after the end of the Civil War. The members of the Gun Club are in a very depressed state. Nobody cares about building bigger and better guns anymore. The club is in danger of extinction. Then the president, Impey Barbicane, summons the members together for an important announcement. He calls attention to the deplorably low state of activity into which the Gun Club has fallen since the cessation of hostilities. He now proposes to remedy this situation. His plan is to build a big cannon, a *really* big cannon. A cannon big enough to send a projectile all the way to the moon! The announcement is received with wild enthusiasm. And the Gun Club immediately proceeds to put its plan into execution.

First, a message is sent to the Cambridge Observatory requesting information on the moon. The astronomers there reply that the distance of the moon at the closest approach, or perigee, is 218,657 miles, or 22,000 miles less than its average distance. It is not necessary, however, to give the projectile a velocity sufficient to send it the entire distance to the moon, but only to the neutral point where lunar and terrestrial gravitation are equal. An initial velocity of 36,000 feet per second (6.81 miles per second) will enable the projectile to attain this point. The cannon should be pointed toward the zenith at some place between

0° and 28° north or south latitude where the moon passes overhead. It will take eighty-three hours and twenty minutes to reach the neutral point if the projectile is fired when the moon is at perigee.

It is said that Verne got his brother-in-law, who was a professor of mathematics, to help him with the technical part. If so, he does not appear to have worked very hard, for the book abounds in errors. (The reader who is interested in pursuing the subject further should consult the articles in *Popular Astronomy* for 1942 by Laurence J. Lafleur.) We will pass over the effect of air resistance which would have reduced the projectile to a flaming meteor soon after it left the cannon's mouth. In fact, the force of friction would have been so great that it is doubtful if the projectile would ever have been able to climb out of the cannon at all. Verne was well aware of the action of friction for he estimates that it would have reduced the speed of the projectile by about a third. But he says practically nothing about its heating effect. He merely remarks that the atmosphere would be pierced so quickly that no appreciable heat would be produced. Of course, if the heating effect of friction had been considered realistically, there would never have been any story in the first place. We can legitimately write this omission off as dramatic license.

Other errors are not so easily dismissed. In speaking about the neutral point Verne says that its position depends upon the *densities* of the earth and moon. If their densities were equal this point would be midway between them. But when their different densities are taken into consideration, this point is found to be 47/60 (78 per cent) of the whole journey, or 186,800 miles from the earth. Now this is entirely wrong. The *densities* of the earth and moon have nothing to do with it. It is their relative *masses* that determine the position of the neutral point. The density of the earth is 1.67 times that of the moon. But the mass of the earth is 81 times that of the moon. This puts the neutral point at 90 per cent of the distance to the moon, or at 216,000 miles from the earth. The mass of the moon was known almost as accurately a century ago as it is today. How Verne arrived at the figure of 47/60 is a mystery.

There is a curious inconsistency in Verne's remarks about where the cannon should be located. He says that it should be sunk in the earth pointing directly upward when the moon is at perigee. This launching point should be somewhere between 28° north and south latitude, which takes into account the greatest range of the moon north and south of the equator. But if the cannon is to be aimed for the moon at perigee it cannot simply be *anywhere* between 28° N. and 28° S. The cannon must be in the same latitude as the declination of the moon when it is at perigee. Suppose when the moon is at perigee its declination is 18° N. Then the cannon must be located somewhere along the parallel of latitude 18° N. Only at this latitude would the moon pass through the zenith at perigee. And the time the moon reaches perigee would fix the longitude of the point. Verne says nothing about the time when the moon reaches perigee or what its longitude should be. He located the cannon in Florida apparently because it is within the United States and less than 28° N. of the equator.

To determine whether the projectile lands on the moon, an observatory with a telescope 192 inches in aperture is erected on Longs Peak in the territory of Missouri. This telescope is expected to magnify 48,000 times, bringing the moon within an optical distance of 5 miles, and enabling astronomers to discern an object on its surface 9 feet in diameter and 15 feet long, the size of the projectile.

Here Verne reveals his complete ignorance of telescopes and the observations that can be made with them. For it would be utterly impossible to see anything on the moon or anywhere else at a magnification of 48,000. The magnification that can be used on a telescope is severely limited by the turbulence of the atmosphere. The atmosphere is continually disturbed by rising and descending currents of air of different densities. As a result, when the moon or other object is viewed through a telescope the image appears to be in a state of agitation, shimmering like an object seen through the heated air rising over a fire. These air currents produce the twinkling of the stars. The more magnification you use on a telescope the more you magnify this twinkling. If you use too much magnification the agitation gets so bad that the image becomes simply a blurred smear. For this reason a magnification of about 1,000 is all that can be used to advantage on any telescope, regardless of its size. Even supposing the telescope were capable of sighting the projectile, how would the astronomers ever have been able to pick it up? Imagine scanning millions of square miles of lunar surface trying to detect a marking just on the limit of visibility. To be detected, the projectile should have made a bright flash on contact, or released a dye that would have left a large colored spot on the surface.

It is hard to understand what useful purpose would have been served in 1870 by sending a projectile to the moon. Today a rocket sent to the moon or near the moon can radio back useful information. But merely landing a projectile on the moon would have resulted in nothing of value—merely the satisfaction of doing it. Verne, being a good story teller, fully realized this and took steps to modify the situation accordingly.

Shortly before the launching, an enthusiastic Frenchman, Michel Arden, wires Barbicane that he intends to go to the moon in a hollow conical projectile fired from the cannon. An exciting encounter comes next, in which Barbicane is attacked by his old enemy, Captain Nicholl, who declares the whole project to be insane and doomed to failure. Michel Arden finally secures peace between them by persuading them to accompany him to the moon so they can see for themselves if all goes according to schedule. Thus *From the Earth to the Moon* ends with the three intrepid adventurers being hurled into space from the mouth of the cannon. The world had to wait five years for *Round the Moon* to learn what happened to them, but now the two can be read together in *Trip to the Moon.*

When only a few minutes out, they narrowly escape collision with what appears to be an asteroid. Barbicane informs them that it is really a second satellite of the earth, discovered by a M. Pettit, who has calculated its orbital elements. It revolves around the earth in a period of three hours and twenty minutes at a distance of 4,650 miles from the surface. (Needless to say this second satellite is pure invention. A few years ago an exhaustive search was made for a second satellite of the earth without result.) These figures are wrong, for a simple calculation from Kepler's third law shows that a satellite revolving 4,650 miles from the surface would have a period of four hours and thirty minutes. For the period to be three hours and twenty minutes the satellite would have had to revolve 3,075 miles from the surface. The travelers soon forget the encounter with the satellite but it has important consequences later on.

In *Round the Moon,* Verne meets with the same writing problem that faced Poe in "Hans Pfaal"; he has to keep a story going when little is happening. But Verne is quite successful at inventing interesting incidents. The tap on the oxygen apparatus is left open so that the travelers become intoxicated from the gas and finally fall to the floor insensible. There seems to be no medical evidence that an overdose of oxygen will produce a state akin to drunkenness but it makes an amusing chapter. Two dogs, forerunners of "Laika," are taken along in the projectile. One is injured at the take-off and dies. They dispose of its body by the simple process of opening a shutter in the wall of the projectile and thrusting it outside. This would have been a fatal maneuver, for no matter how quickly it was done, practically all the air would have escaped.

Upon reaching the neutral point between the earth and moon the force of gravity momentarily disappears, and everything within the projectile becomes weightless. The travelers set three glasses in space before them, fill them with wine from a bottle, and drink a toast to the success of their trip. But since the projectile was moving freely under gravity, the travelers would have been weightless during the entire trip and not merely at the neutral point. They could not have poured wine from a bottle but would have had to suck it out with straws. By shaking the bottle they might have forced the wine out causing it to circulate around the cabin in great globules. They might have captured these globules in their mouth but it would have been an awkward maneuver for a connoisseur of fine vintages.

As the projectile nears the moon it becomes increasingly evident that it is never going to reach the surface but is pursuing quite a different orbit than the one planned for it. Why this mysterious deviation from the calculated path? The travelers wrack their brains. Then Barbicane gets an idea. It was that second satellite! Its gravitational attraction pulled them off their course causing them to pursue an orbit around the moon instead of to the moon. For a while they fear they are destined to revolve endlessly through space as a satellite of a satellite. They make a last desperate attempt at a lunar landing by firing rockets attached to the hull when they reach the neutral point again. But instead of precipitating them onto the moon, the impetus given the projectile sends it in the opposite direction. As a result, they begin a fall 160,000 miles back to the earth.

The scene switches to a vessel making soundings in deep water off the coast of lower California. A flaming meteor plunges out of the sky taking off the ship's bowsprit as it falls. The sailors are convinced it is the projectile returned to earth again. They comb the bottom of the ocean searching for it but to no avail. Then suddenly it occurs to them that since the projectile is hollow it could not possibly sink. Eventually they find it floating serenely on the surface with the hatch open, through which can be heard the voices of the travelers playing at dominoes. The travelers are rescued. There is a big banquet to celebrate their safe return. The Gun Club goes ahead with more ambitious plans for "Interstellary" communication.

Trip to the Moon was one of Verne's earliest and most successful novels. Verne, however, had the misfortune to live just at the wrong time. His writing was all done before the big discoveries of the present age: radium, wireless, X rays, and the vacuum tube. As a result, his fictional effects had to be achieved with energy in its cruder forms. Yet for this reason there is a certain charm about these Victorian romances which undoubtedly contributed to the success of such pictures as *Around the World in Eighty Days* and *Twenty Thousand Leagues Under the Sea*. To Verne goes the credit of trying to get us to the moon by a halfway rational method which still sounds plausible even if a close reading does reveal a multitude of errors.

Thirty-five years passed before another notable moon story appeared. In this story, the hero goes to the moon not by any mechanical device, but by pure magic in the form of antigravity.* The idea of antigravity is older than you might think. It first seems to have been used by Professor George Tucker of the University of Virginia, writing under the name of J. Atterly, who published *A Voyage to the Moon* in 1827. Tucker had Poe as a student for a year and may possibly have influenced him in writing "Hans Pfaal." Atterly's hero finds a metal with a tendency to fly away from the earth, and by coating a vessel with it succeeds in reaching the moon. Antigravity turns up again in a book by Kurd Lasswitz entitled *Auf Zwei Planeten,* published in 1897. Lasswitz, who was a professor of mathematics at Jena, not only employed antigravity, but also explosive repulsive systems and space stations, all of which he worked out in great detail. The book enjoyed wide popularity in Germany, but was never translated into English, so that it is hard to say how much it may have influenced subsequent English and American writers.

* For the remarks about Tucker and Lasswitz, I am indebted to an article by Arthur C. Clarke entitled "Space-Travel in Fact and Fiction," published in the *Journal of the British Interplanetary Society* for September, 1950.

In 1901 H. G. Wells wrote *The First Men in the Moon* in which he also employed a marvelous antigravity compound called Cavorite for launching his two characters into space. Cavorite is a synthetic substance, named after one of the characters, which acts as a screen against gravity in the same way that asbestos acts as a screen against light and heat. Cavor and the character who relates the story construct a sphere covered with blinds of Cavorite which can be raised and lowered at will. Pulling down the blinds on the side facing the earth automatically causes the ship to leave the surface and fly away into space. Going to the moon, as Wells relates it, sounds like a simple enough operation. "And then we had to discuss and decide what provisions we were to take—compressed foods, concentrated essences, steel cylinders containing reserve oxygen, an arrangement for removing carbonic acid and waste from the air and restoring oxygen by means of sodium peroxide, water condensers, and so forth. I remember the little heap they made in the corner—tins, and rolls, and boxes—convincingly matter-of-fact." Compare this with the elaborate preparations for launching one of the seven selected astronauts into space today!

Stepping behind a screen of Cavorite must have been a remarkable experience. At the surface of the earth the force of gravity is one g, amounting to an acceleration of 32 feet per second per second. To go from one g to zero g, a person would have to be lifted out to about a million miles from the earth (theoretically to infinity). Naturally it would take a tremendous amount of energy to do this. So you might argue it would take a prodigiously strong man to step behind a screen of Cavorite. It is said that somebody once called Wells' attention to this fact much to his annoyance. As if he didn't know it already!

The two travelers take off for the moon and arrive without mishap. Here we should stress that the title of the book is *The First Men in the Moon* and not *The First Men on the Moon*. For after some preliminary investigation the travelers discover that the moon is just a hollow shell in which the Selenites dwell, only a few coming out occasionally to graze their cattle. The craters, whose nature has so long puzzled astronomers, are simply openings in the surface made by the insect people below. The Selenites, incidentally, bear a remarkably close resemblance to the Morlocks, created by Wells in his *The Time Machine*. This idea of an undercover civilization seems to have fascinated Wells, since he used it in two of his novels, and in some of his other works he refers to the increasing number of installations below ground found in modern society.

The First Men in the Moon never attained the popularity of some of Wells' other novels of science fiction such as *The War of the Worlds, The Time Machine,* and *The Invisible Man.* The first and last parts of the story, in fact, are badly dated, but the major section dealing with the travelers' adventures on the moon is still interesting. In my opinion, Wells writes in a more engaging style than either Poe or Verne, possibly because he is more modern. *The First Men in the Moon* has a sort of wide-eyed quality about it, a sense of wonder, which is often lacking in science fiction today. Let us hope that we never lose it completely.

Beginning in the late twenties and early thirties several science fiction magazines appeared on the newsstands carrying stories in which travel to the moon and planets was a common procedure. By this time it had become well established that the only practical method of getting into outer space was by means of the rocket. Hence, in these stories the characters almost invariably traveled by rocket, although there was no assurance that this means of transportation would ever be more than a dream. Furthermore, authors were getting tired of devoting a lot of wordage to space travel itself, and were more concerned with relating what happened to their characters after they reached their destination. In other words, the trip from one planet to another was taken pretty much for granted. If you wanted a character to travel from San Francisco to New York, you would hardly spend ten thousand words describing his train trip across the country. The reader is quite willing to assume that such a trip is possible. Space travel rapidly followed the same course.

These early science fiction stories frequently took the form of a boy-and-girl exploration of a planet accompanied by an old professor who acted as a sort of combination chaperon and technical adviser. Gradually these gave way to yarns of a more sophisticated type involving the sociological consequences of attempts to colonize a planet. Sometimes authors grew tired of using the same old locales in the solar system and roamed far afield to planets revolving around the stars, where they could conjure up any kind of wonders they pleased. Spaceships grew until they became commodious enough to accommodate a whole colony of passengers. Trips to the stars were complicated by the fact that they were so long that the original passengers had no hope of reaching the end of the line. But they had children and after their death their children had children until at last their remote ancestors stepped off the ship onto some strange planet. There was always the danger in this step method of transportation from generation to generation, that the remote descendants of the original travelers would forget why they started out in the first place. Some authors found even nuclear rocket power too sluggish, so that they sent their heroes to the stars by paraphysical means with the speed of thought. If this method can be made to work it certainly transcends all others in ease and economy of space travel.

Since most stories of a trip to the moon have enjoyed considerable success, it seems strange that so few motion pictures have been produced dealing with this subject. Doubtless, producers have had their minds on the more familiar subjects of love, marriage, murder, and seduction, with little thought of such faraway topics as the moon. Yet it is interesting to note that one of the very first motion pictures ever made in 1902 dealt with a trip to the moon. It was a short novelty number that made no pretense of being realistic. The producer was a Frenchman named George Mieles, who had a natural flair for special effects and who discovered (or stumbled upon) most of the tricks in photography used at present.

Fascinated by science fiction, Mieles depicted the moon with a face. Girls in tights are shown touching off a charge that sends a projectile into space. (In his pictures Mieles frequently employed girls from the Folies-Bergère for decorative purposes.) The projectile hits the Man in the Moon in the eye much to his discomfort. Mieles was far ahead of his time in the technique of making pictures, but unfortunately, he had little business sense when it came to marketing them. Thus he sold his pictures outright instead of resorting to the much more profitable procedure of renting them. The result was that he eventually lost everything and was finally reduced to hawking newspapers on the streets of Paris. Today his name is known only to a few students of the history of the cinema.

We have to wait many years in fact, before we come to a motion picture about a trip to the moon which deals with the subject in a serious way. This picture was *Frau im Mond* ("Girl in the Moon"), which was produced in Germany, and which had its world première in Berlin on October 15, 1929. It was directed by Fritz Lang, who had a great reputation in Germany at that time, and who later came to the United States where he also directed with success. Willy Ley has given a detailed account of the efforts to publicize the picture.* The idea was that if a giant-size, real rocket could be fired about the time of the première, it could hardly fail to attract wide attention. Hermann Oberth, as the greatest rocket expert of the time, had been called to Berlin by Fritz Lang to act as scientific adviser for the motion picture. The project appealed to Oberth as a possible means of getting funds for rocket experimentation. The trouble was that Oberth was a theoretical man with no practical experience in putting a real rocket together. Also, he was a stranger in Berlin and had no notion where to find assistants. According to Ley, the project ended in complete confusion and no rocket was ever fired.

The reader will find frequent references to *Frau im Mond* scattered through the literature of rocketry but nowhere will you find a word as to what the picture is about. Who was the "Girl in the Moon"? How did she get there? Why did she go to the moon in the first place? Willy Ley, who, with Oberth, was one of the original technical advisers on the film, was kind enough to write a synopsis. Since there seems to be nothing on record about the film, the synopsis is reproduced here in full for the benefit of those who are interested in the history of rocketry.

> Old Professor Mansfeldt still believes in Hansen's theory about the discrepancy between the two hemispheres of the moon. According to this idea, the moon is egg-shaped with the long pointed end oriented in the direction of the

* *Rockets, Missiles, and Space Travel*, pp. 124-130.

earth. The moon may be regarded as a mountain peak with its base on the far side and its top on the near side. Because the center of gravity is on the far side, all the air has collected there. Mansfeldt feels that the far side may hold riches, gold, and possibly ruins of a former culture.

Wolf Helius has devoted his fortune to financing rocket research. Already a circumlunar rocket has brought back evidence that Mansfeldt is correct about the far side of the moon. The first spaceship is now nearly finished. The plans for this ship are mostly the work of Hans Windegger who is in charge of construction, and who will be the copilot, with Wolf Helius as pilot. Friede Velten, an astronomy student, is the fiancée of Windegger.

About a month before take-off Mansfeldt is approached by a man who says, "Call me Walt Turner, this name will serve as well as any other." He wants to buy the manuscript of Mansfeldt's book but Mansfeldt throws him out. Wolf Helius happens to arrive at the moment and saves Turner from breaking his neck. Helius then persuades Mansfeldt to move in with him till take-off time. This Mansfeldt proceeds to do, bringing along with him his pet mouse, Josephine. (The only purpose of putting Josephine in the story seems to be to point up the character of Professor Mansfeldt.)

Evidently, Turner has stolen the plans for the rocket and the films of the moon's far side, for he informs Helius that the people for whom he is working will not return them unless he is taken along on the trip to the moon. The others, feeling that nothing can be done, decide to include Turner as a member of the crew.

The night before the take-off several of the passengers have varied emotional experiences. Friede and Windegger realize that they are not suited to each other. Mansfeldt sees himself as a boy in grade school again compelled to defend his ideas against his teacher's sarcasm. Wolf Helius dreams that he meets the Wandering Jew who encourages him.

The rocket is fired at night. Here for the first time Fritz Lang used the count down to add to the dramatic suspense. After take-off they discover that the eleven-year-old son of the janitor is on board as a stowaway. They land on the far side of the moon without much trouble, where they find that air is present.

Mansfeldt wanders off by himself and falls to his death down a deep cavern. Everybody is wondering what Turner is really after. He is most interested in the ship and Windegger finally realizes that he intends to steal the ship and leave the rest of them marooned on the moon. (Another ship is being built but is by no means finished yet.) There is a gunfight between Windegger and Turner in which Turner is shot. Turner gets off a shot himself which at first seems to have missed its mark. Then they discover it has hit one of the oxygen lines in the ship, and by the time this is noticed, most of the ship's oxygen has escaped. Since there is not enough oxygen left to carry them all back to earth, Helius decides to remain behind while he waits for the rescue ship. He gives the girl and boy instructions on how to handle the automatic controls. Friede is especially careful that the boy understands this.

Helius watches the rocket take off for earth. Rescue for him will come in a couple of months. As he turns away he finds that Friede Velten has elected to stay behind with him.

It is hard to form any critical estimate of *Frau im Mond* from this bare outline. The girl in the moon does not sound as if she had much to do with what went on there. (It is hard to understand why a young student of astronomy would be taken to the moon in the first place.) The motivation for going to the moon is also obscure. Nobody would go for any riches that might be there. The cost of transportation is so prohibitive that nothing on the moon could be of sufficient intrinsic value to justify a trip for that purpose alone.

Frau im Mond ran serially in the weekly *Die Woche* in 1928, and was later published as a book which was translated into English. The film, however, was never shown in the United States.

After *Frau im Mond* there is another long wait before the appearance of a moon picture. During the depression, men's thoughts were far away from outer space and during World War II motion pictures were mostly concerned either directly or incidentally with the war and its various repercussions on humanity. With the end of hostilities, however, people were eager for plays that would amuse them and take their minds off the horrors of the recent conflict. Stories of the escape type were much in demand. About this time there also came an extraordinary boom in science fiction, undoubtedly encouraged by remarkable technical wartime achievements such as radar, the atomic bomb, and especially the V-2 rocket. It is not surprising, therefore, that a motion picture dealing with a trip to the moon finally made its appearance. Perhaps the surprising thing is that it was so long in coming. This picture was *Destination Moon*, produced by George Pal as an independent in 1950, with a script based on a story by the well-known science fiction writer Robert Heinlein, and with sets designed by Chesley Bonestell.

Destination Moon was the first serious attempt to depict a flight to the moon with close attention to authentic detail. Within the limitations imposed by the budget and the effects that could be created within the studio, this was not easy to do. As Heinlein himself remarked in an article about the picture, "The best way to photograph space flight convincingly is to raise a few million dollars, get together a scientific and engineering staff of the calibre used to make the atom bomb, take over the facilities of General Electric, White Sands, and Douglas Aircraft, and *build* a spaceship. Then go along and photograph what happens. . . . We had to use the second-best method—which meant that every shot, save for a few before take-off from Earth, involved special effects, trick photography, and unheard-of lighting problems." Since the technicians were facing these problems for the first time, they had little or nothing to guide them. As might be expected therefore, there were certain incongruities in the picture which were corrected later in other films produced by George Pal. As it was, however, *Destination Moon* established a standard of excellence for others to shoot at for a long time to come.

The rocket, launched into space with four passengers aboard, landed in the lunar crater Harpalus [Plate VIII] in the Cold Sea near the lunar north pole. Harpalus was selected because even at noon the temperature never rises above a moderate 80° F. It lies in a region of lowlands and highlands where the travelers would have had a variety of scenery to explore. A whole huge sound stage was devoted to the interior of this crater, which looked quite realistic except for the cracks on the floor. These were a couple of inches wide and why they were put there nobody seemed to know. It is true that there are long cracks in the moon's surface several miles wide called rills, but they are not like cracks in dried mud that were in the floor of Harpalus. My young daughter, while walking over the set, got her foot stuck in one of these cracks and for a while it looked as if she were permanently caught on the moon. I took away a loose piece of plaster from the set, and for several days this reposed on my desk as the nearest thing I would ever have to a piece of the moon. One morning I came to my office and found it missing. I suspect the janitor thought it was a piece of plaster that fell off the ceiling and threw it away when he came in to dust.

It is a wonder that some object didn't show up on the lunar surface in *Destination Moon* that was not supposed to be there. Usually studios do not encourage visitors on the set, but in the last days of filming *Destination Moon* it seemed as if most of the space enthusiasts in Los Angeles were there. Watching a motion picture being made is a rather tedious business. It is interesting while a scene is actually being filmed, but there are long monotonous waits between shots, and the audience has to pass the time the best way it can. As a result, the surface of the moon gradually became littered with cigarette stubs and Coke bottles. Usually before they shot a scene somebody would clean up the moon, but there was always the chance of a stray Coke bottle lurking behind a crater.

In *Destination Moon* the travelers wore space suits that were as authentic as it was possible to make them at that time. The hole in the front of the helmet was left vacant in the long shots, but in the close-ups they were glassed in and the actors had to depend upon their oxygen tanks just as if they were actually on the moon. The interior of the spaceship looked very realistic with dials on the walls and other pieces of equipment of the type that would be expected in such a vehicle. There were scenes on the way to the moon showing the passengers floating about in a state of free fall. The great leaps one could take on the moon owing to its lesser surface gravity were illustrated by midgets hitched to a special harness which sent them flying over the set. The picture was so good that even the members of the British Interplanetary Society, who are the most critical people in the world, were lavish in their praise.

Predictions are always rash, but it seems unlikely that there will be any more stories or motion pictures dealing primarily with a trip to the moon or planets.

We are too close to reality now to make such material of much interest. About everything ficitional has been said on film that can be said on the subject.

Some may contend that these imaginative accounts of travel to the moon served no useful purpose except to amuse people, and may have done actual harm in giving them misleading ideas about space travel. Yet they stirred men's imagination and served to keep the idea of travel beyond the earth alive during the long dark years when it seemed very remote indeed. There can be no doubt that Jules Verne's *Trip to the Moon* with all its faults has exerted a powerful effect on human thought in preparing our minds for this greatest of all adventures. We regarded the launching of the artificial satellites with sympathy as well as the keenest interest. Our space program will run into billions of dollars. Nobody has promised us that there will be any direct dollars and cents return. Yet almost everybody seems to be in favor of getting a man to the moon, the quicker the better. Of course, it is impossible to predict where interplanetary exploration may lead us. When Columbus sailed for the New World no one could have predicted that his voyage would lead to the discovery of the biggest oil field in the world. Today we are just as incapable of foreseeing the ultimate results of travel to the moon.

THE MOON IN

MODERN ASTRONOMY

*

* The Formation of the Craters

The chief difficulty in writing about the origin of the lunar craters is the appalling number of hypotheses that have been advanced to explain them. Apparently everybody who has looked at the moon has had a try at it. Some of these explanations sound like plain crank ideas. Others are undeniably ingenious. But today there is only one that seems acceptable to us—the meteoritic impact hypothesis. It is ironical to think that when this hypothesis was first advanced more than a century ago, it was regarded merely as a scientific curiosity, an idea too far-fetched for serious consideration. In its original form the hypothesis was quite different from our present conception of it. The craters were supposed to have been formed when the surface of the moon was in a plastic condition. The meteorite gouged out a hole like a rock striking a mud bank. The fact that a meteorite would strike the surface with the explosive violence of a bomb was not appreciated until modern times. This alone would not have caused the meteoritic impact hypothesis to be considered as more than a reasonable possibility. Evidence of a more convincing nature was forthcoming when Baldwin showed that there was a continuous relationship between the width and depth of terrestrial bomb craters and the lunar craters. Of course, this did not constitute proof that the lunar craters were blasted out by meteoritic impact. It merely made the idea seem more acceptable from analogy with something we can produce and measure on the earth.

It has long been tacitly assumed that the moon (and all the planets, for that matter) were at one time in a molten state, a kind of a hangover from our feeling that the planets must somehow have originated as flaming offspring of the sun. Cosmologists, however, now incline to the view that the planets grew by accretion, never went through a molten phase, and remained cold throughout their entire history. Suppose the moon grew by accretion of the meteoritic debris it encountered in space. Then the craters would seem to be the product of the last stage of this sweeping-up process, when the moon had reached its present size, but collisions with large meteorites were still occurring frequently. Of course, the earth underwent the same bombardment, but the effects were soon obliterated by erosion. Eventually the space around the earth and moon was swept clean of debris. Evolution by meteoritic impact is now an idea of the past.

*

The Formation of the Craters

ROBERT S. RICHARDSON

THE moon is so close to the earth that, when viewed through a large tele-scope under favorable conditions, surface markings of only a few hundred feet in extent can be discerned. The most remarkable surface features are the craters, of which thirty thousand have been mapped. These range in diameter from mere dots of a mile to great walled plains 140 miles across, such as Clavius [Plate X] and Grimaldi. Certain portions of the moon's surface, such as the region around the south pole, are so thickly studded with craters that there seems to be no end to them, while the dark, smooth "seas" near-by are practically free of them. Besides the craters and seas, there are several jagged mountain ranges with peaks rising to 25,000 feet, rivaling the most lofty eleva-tions on the earth. At full moon the long, bright "rays" radiating from such craters as Tycho [Plate XII] and Copernicus [Plate XV] are a conspicuous feature.

From our brief survey we can assert positively that, in agreement with tele-scopic observations, no changes of consequence are occurring on the moon now. The pockmarked condition of the surface clearly indicates, however, that changes of a cataclysmic nature obviously occurred at some time in the remote past. *Something* must have happened to produce all those craters. There has been no lack of theories to explain what that *something* was. It is really amazing how many ways people can devise for creating a solar system and for making a crater on the moon. The earliest explanation, as might be expected, was that the craters are extinct volcanoes, a theory which still has its adherents today. Upon close examination, however, the lunar craters are found to have only a superficial resemblance to terrestrial volcanoes. Not only are they vastly larger than terrestrial volcanoes, but there are important differences in structure as well. Volcanoes are pointed, cone-shaped structures with a small opening at the top, whereas the lunar craters more nearly resemble shallow basins with gently sloping walls. Some craters are so wide that to an observer at their center the surrounding wall would be out of sight below the horizon.

A second hypothesis has the craters formed by enormous bubbles of gas rising

Robert S. Richardson, from *Exploring Mars,* McGraw-Hill, New York, 1954, pp. 56-60.

from the interior and bursting when the surface was in a plastic condition, leaving a ring-shaped scar. According to a third, the moon was once covered by a thick sheet of ice. Heat from the interior melted the ice in places, creating cup-shaped depressions. Water from the melting ice evaporated, but before the vapor could escape, it was deposited around the edge, forming a high rim. In view of the fact that the temperature directly under the sun is 214° F., the ice-layer theory seems a bit strained. Even more fantastic is the suggestion that the craters are the work of micro-organisms such as those that built our coral atolls.

The explanation of the craters that seems most plausible is that they are the result of impact due to meteoric bombardment. It is, of course, impossible to make a definite statement until geologists have had an opportunity to study these structures at first hand. But considerable evidence can be adduced for such a view.*

The idea of craters formed by meteoric bombardment is an old one, apparently having been first advanced by the German astronomer Gruithuisen in 1822, but it seems to have won few converts. The impact hypothesis was again advanced in 1873 by Proctor, who is usually given credit for being its originator. In 1909, T.J.J. See went even further and declared that the battered surface of the moon was caused by the absorption and impact, not of meteorites, but of satellites! In 1948, Ralph B. Baldwin presented new evidence in favor of the meteoric impact hypothesis, although not in the form in which it was originally conceived. Proctor thought of the craters as being formed by meteorites striking the surface when it was still in a plastic condition and leaving a hole similar to that produced by hurling a pebble into mud. Baldwin has shown, on the other hand, that the assumption of a semiplastic surface is unnecessary. The collision would occur with such violence that the portion of the meteorite in contact with the surface would be vaporized, the effect being essentially the same as in the explosion of a bomb. In the original theory the craters were supposed to have been formed simply by the mechanical force of the meteorite's gouging a hole in the soft ground. It was not realized that the high velocities of the meteorites would blow gigantic holes in the rocky crust far larger than the bodies that produced them.

Such an argument would not be especially convincing without additional evidence. Such evidence has been obtained from measures on terrestrial bomb craters, which show a definite relationship between their width and depth. Baldwin's contribution consists in showing that the same relationship holds for craters on the moon. In fact, if the curve for terrestrial bomb craters is extended, it fits directly onto that for the lunar craters, forming a continuous unbroken sequence. Baldwin is convinced that the lunar craters are essentially

* It must be emphasized that *all* selenologists do not accept the meteoritic impact theory of the origin of the lunar craters. They believe many craters are much too regularly disposed to be the result of random impact.

the same as man-made bomb craters, except that most of them are on a vastly larger scale.

Not only the craters, but also the dark, smooth seas are believed to have been formed by collision. In the case of the seas, however, the colliding body was not a meteorite but rather a planetesimal several hundred miles in diameter, perhaps one of T.J.J. See's satellites. The collision reduced the planetesimal to a pool of molten lava, which flowed over the surface as a flat sheet, covering and filling the craters in that region. The smooth surface solidified and later was again bombarded by meteorites, which formed new craters. These were filled by other lava flows from planetesimals, and the process continued until gradually space in the vicinity of the earth and moon was cleared and the face of our satellite was left with its present aspect.

There are reasons for believing that the great crater Tycho in the southern hemisphere was the last important feature added to the moon's surface. The long white streaks radiating from Tycho, so bright as to be visible to the un-aided eye at full moon, are believed to consist of dust thrown out at the time of the explosion. The exceptional length of the rays indicates that the explosion was of tremendous violence and that at the time it occurred, the moon, as now, had no atmosphere. One ray is so long that it can be traced across the Mare Serenitatis into the northern hemisphere and around the limb out of sight into the invisible hemisphere. On examintion, a ray may be found on the opposite limb, apparently a continuation of the one across the Mare Serenitatis. The slight displacement in the positions of the rays may be explained as the result of the moon's rotation while the dust was traveling around the globe. From the amount of the displacement it has been calculated that the period of the moon's rotation when Tycho was formed must have been greater than twelve days, instead of twenty-seven days as at present.

* The Fall of the Meteorite

The impact of the meteorites that produced the lunar craters must be numbered as among the most interesting events in the history of the earth-moon system. What a sight it must have been to have watched the lunar craters in the process of being born [Plates V, VI]. Today we can only look at the moon and attempt to reconstruct the cataclysmic events that produced the battered surface that we see.

In this extract from *The Face of the Moon* Ralph Baldwin has reconstructed for us the succession of events that resulted from the fall of the Mare Imbrium planetesimal. The material is of such a spectacular nature that it is impossible to set it down except in terms that naturally fall into dramatic form. The meteorite bores a hole in the surface, a moment of calm prevails, then an inferno breaks loose as the surface layers rise and split apart like a gigantic flower. It is all the more dramatic because the whole upheaval occurs in silence! The detail with which the author recounts the holocaust is clear evidence of the time devoted to thinking through each step in the physical processes involved. Whether one agrees with the author on each of the steps is of minor importance. The extract makes good reading for its literary quality alone. At any rate, *something* of the sort described here must have happened to have produced the placid surface that we know today as the Sea of Rains [Plate IV].

The Circular Maria

RALPH B. BALDWIN

LET us review the complete process. Before the impact Mare Imbrium and all the appended lava flows did not exist. Mare Serenitatis [Plate IX] was present, probably not lava-filled, but bordered by two proud and high ranges, the Haemus Mountains and the Caucasus. The southern section of Serenitatis looked much as portions of the northern half do now, spotted with craters, many of them blurred and overlapping. Where Mare Imbrium was to come was a broad upland, dotted with thousands of craters large and small. Sinus Iridum [Plate VIII] had not yet raised its massive ramparts to catch the morning sun.

Downward the meteorite plummeted from the northeast, gradually gaining velocity. Probably it did not even glow from the effect of the nearly absent lunar atmosphere. Then it struck the surface and quickly disappeared beneath, leaving a small sharp hole to mark its passage. For only an instant, however, did the calm prevail, for then all hell broke loose, soundlessly, on a scale to shame the infernos dreamed of by little men. A great section of the crust, several hundreds of miles across, domed up, split rapidly and radially from the central point. Surface layers peeled back on themselves like the opening of a gigantic flower, followed quickly by a stamen of dust and fragments spreading rapidly in all directions without the rolling turbulence imparted by an atmosphere.

The unfolding of the initial dome had a shielding effect and thus created a null zone surrounding the great pit. Most of the matter lifted from the crater was deposited in this protected area, raising a broad and low rim of mountains. Higher-velocity fragments, spewed forth nearly horizontally, smashed great furrows into the moon's face during the succeeding twenty minutes, furrows radiating outward from the explosion focus. Some of these bodies were the ones which so nearly obliterated the Haemus Mountains.

The activity dies down. Some matter had exceeded the velocity of escape and was henceforth lost to the moon. Other fragments struck, ricocheted, struck again, and came to rest. Dust and larger blocks rained down on all portions of the moon. Soon all was quiet. The chasm just born was about 350 miles across

Ralph B. Baldwin, from *The Face of the Moon*, University of Chicago Press, Chicago, 1949, pp. 210-213.

and perhaps 6 or 7 miles deep relative to the curving surface. Actually it probably was slightly convex rather than concave, for the moon is a rather small body.

Surrounding the crater the rim was quite unsymmetrical. In the north its width was about 100 miles. On the face which now forms the Apennines, opposite the direction of approach of the meteorite, it was over twice as wide and correspondingly more jagged. The extreme roughness of the mountainous border makes it evident that its materials were emplaced violently.

The first of the two major changes in the moon was the crater and its rim. The second was far more subtle. When the meteorite struck, not only did it release bountiful supplies of energy, but it transmitted a tremendous quantity of momentum. The crust of the moon absorbed this shock; it had to, but when the pressure was released, a tremendous rebound followed. A great segment moved upward forming a mound, which, being completely damped by tension fractures, became fixed as a structural dome. The crater was perched slightly north of center.

This massive dome, 800 miles across, was completely surrounded by a ring syncline. Still farther away a weak ring anticline was raised, forming the outer edge of the syncline. This is the exact pattern always found when elastic substances are suddenly disturbed.

An appreciable interval of time passed before the next stage in the drama unfolded. A large meteorite fell, and the crater Archimedes arose to mark its passing. A still larger body formed that near-duplicate of Clavius [Plate X] whose remains we now know as Sinus Iridum. Both structures developed on the dome.

And then the great central block of the dome, nearly circular, began to settle. Long held higher than hydrostatic pressure would permit by the strength of its own rocks acting as keystones, the mass slipped downward. Ring faults, probably formed during the raising of the mound, acted as slides. The Apennine section dropped a good 10,000 to 12,000 feet, perhaps more. The opposite face slid nearly as far. Sinus Iridum split in two, one half remaining on the raised rim of the new and larger Mare Imbrium pit, the other dropping deep into the abyss.

As the great millstone sank, huge columns of superheated magma welled and bubbled up, probably coming mainly from the ring faults. As at a great reservoir, the liquid filled the vast depression, buried the moon's greatest crater until only an indicated ring of isolated mountain peaks remained to mark its rim, then burst its bonds to the east and spread rapidly out to produce Mare Nubium and Oceanus Procellarum. North and south, the liquid sped around the mountains into the ring syncline where it buried many craters and splash craters. On the west, the gap between Caucasus and Apennine ranges offered easy ingress to Mare Serenitatis, whose southern floor was soon covered. Beyond the Haemus Mountains the lavas raced, filling Mare Tranquillitatis, Mare Foecunditatis, and even stretching a ribbon into the basin centered in the Altai Mountains, thus bringing Mare Nectaris into being.

To the far west, little isostatic compensation occurred; the sheets were relatively thin. Mare Serenitatis was an ancient structure of the Imbrian type. Its floor sank somewhat under the new load, as the height measures of Franz have shown. The once level liquid surface now shows a decided slope down from Mare Tranquillitatis into Mare Serenitatis [Plate IX].

To the east the main mass of the magma poured. East of Mare Imbrium the crust sank considerably. It is even possible that the load caused so great an adjustment to occur relatively quickly that the eastern mountain border disappeared beneath the surface except for the scattered Harbinger peaks. The steady eastward dip of the Carpathians and the mountains on the northeast of Mare Imbrium support this view. However, in all cases the main isostatic adjustment was a gradual process which developed its main action after the lavas had frozen.

A block of 400,000 square miles, the area of Mare Imbrium, sinking 2 miles, must displace 800,000 cubic miles of magma.

Lava flows cover about one third of the visible surface of the moon to a depth averaging about one-half mile, judging from the protruding crater rims. A total volume of lava of approximately 1,000,000 cubic miles is indicated. The agreement is probably better than we have any right to expect.

At least three separate sheets of lava spread from Mare Imbrium. The first was dark and highly mobile; it flowed the greatest distance. Somewhat later a lighter-colored lava rose and painted a thin coat over western Mare Imbrium and all save the border of the primal flow in Mare Serenitatis. From the region of Sinus Iridum, another dark flow outlined the northeastern quadrant of Mare Imbrium. The lost half of Sinus Iridum can be traced by low ridges on this lava.

It is necessary to know whether or not the lava could remain liquid long enough to cover the wide expanses now called maria. If not, then other sources of lava than the Imbrian must be found.

It must be postulated that the lava was extremely fluid because of the distance it spread and because of the confined places into which it penetrated. Consequently, it probably was a basic lava and very hot. Highly acid lavas are more viscous. Basic lavas are usually about 10 per cent denser than acid lavas. Thus the isostatic changes would be augmented, particularly if the bright areas of the moon are acidic in nature.

* *The Role of Volcanism*

We can deduce schemes by which a crater might conceivably have been formed but we are unable to cite independent evidence to prove it. That is one of the best features about the meteoritic impact theory. In some degree it is capable of independent proof, in that there is a consistent relationship between the size and depth of terrestrial bomb craters and lunar craters, indicating strongly that both had a similar origin. In other words, when a large meteorite struck the moon, the result was essentially an explosion like a bomb explosion. But many puzzling details remain to be filled in, such as the varying appearance of the lunar formations at the full and quarter phases, and the presence of central peaks in some of the craters. In this article, Kuiper postulates a period when the structure of many craters was drastically changed due to a general heating of the moon by its own radioactivity, an idea that all authorities would probably not be willing to accept. Undoubtedly much that is conjecture today can only be settled by firsthand, on-the-spot observations. And even then it may not be easy.

*

On the Origin of
the Lunar Surface Features

GERARD P. KUIPER

THE *Lunar Craters.* . . . If one examines the distribution of craters in a region, say, around Tycho [Plate XII], one is impressed by the complete *randomness* of the position of these features. Many of them are *wide, deep holes,* often flat-bottomed, with hardly any walls around them. In such instances, the material was apparently blown out of these holes and scattered

Gerard P. Kuiper, from *Proceedings of the National Academy of Sciences,* 1954.

widely over the moon. These craters appear all to belong to the early, or pre-melting, era. They are inconspicuous at full moon. Tycho itself is a crater of the third, or postmelting, era. Here one sees clearly how the material was *displaced* by the impact. Prominent walls were thrown up on top of a sequence of exposed terraces very similar to Meteor Crater, Arizona, and an unaccount-able number of boulders were thrown to distances up to some four crater di-ameters. Hundreds of these boulders can be clearly distinguished in a large tele-scope under the best conditions, together with a very large number of cuts and grooves which they apparently inflicted on neighboring structures. But, beyond that, the entire neighborhood has a "sandy" appearance, quite contrary to re-gions more remote from Tycho. With proper allowance for scale, one must conclude that the number of ejected boulders runs into many thousands.

If volcanic action were responsible for the lunar craters, one would assume that a hundred or a thousand times *fewer* structures would have sufficed. Fur-thermore, as has been pointed out before, volcanoes would have been *additions to,* and not, as many craters are, subtractions from, the landscape. The craters form a continuous series of sizes and shapes, from the smallest visible to huge Mare Imbrium, as was stressed by Baldwin (though a good relation is obtained only if structures that originated within a given era, say, the postmelting era, are intercompared) . Only the impact hypothesis gives a reasonable explanation of this family of structures. Furthermore, from the circular shape of nearly all craters, one concludes that the impacts caused *explosions*—as has been re-marked by Baldwin and Urey. Volcanism, while clearly not responsible for the major tectonic processes on the moon, has, however, played an important role. Its most obvious effects are shown in the appearance of the full moon (see be-low) , assumed to be the result of metamorphizing the lunar crust by steam and heated solutions coming from below. Further, such features as accompany Crater Hyginus could only be volcanic. Finally, important processes have oc-curred in crater bottoms (see below) , which might be classed as volcanic.

The Full Moon. To an observer who has gained some familiarity with the lunar features seen at the quarter phases [Plate III], the appearance of the full moon is utterly baffling. Some large craters such as Clavius [Plate X] are quite invisible—only some small craters inside it can be found. Other large craters can be recognized with difficulty by their ghostlike outlines. But two groups of new features have gained prominence: (1) a dozen or so large craters, of which Tycho is the most striking, and another dozen medium-sized ray craters; (2) thousands of small, brilliant white specks, the largest of which are either small, perfectly shaped, filled circles or white circular rings with a small, dark central patch. About three days before or after full moon the features in group 2 appear to be conical craters, without appreciable rims. The brilliant, spotless white is limited with perfect precision to the inner slopes of the inverted cones. If the cones are complete (not truncated), they appear as uniformly filled circles at full moon; if they have a flat bottom, as happens in the majority of cases, the bottoms are about as dark as the surroundings and the cones look like white rings, somewhat like the Ring Nebula in Lyra. The perfect regularity of these cones is in striking contrast with the wild and rugged appearance of most lunar structures; they look as if they were turned out on a lathe in a block of white chalk which had first been made dark gray on its surface. Mosting A, used in meridian-circle observations of the moon's position, is one of the most important examples of this class. The bright specks and cones occur almost anywhere, though they seem to have a preference for the equatorial belt of the moon. Those occurring in maria are often *slightly yellow* compared to the spotless white specimens on the continents, somewhat like Wood's region near Crater Aristarchus [Plate XXI].

The perfect, undamaged appearance of the white cones shows that they are among the most recent lunar structures. The same is true for the ray craters. Rays of Copernicus, Kepler, Tycho [Plates II, XII], and some others fall equally on the maria and the continents. These craters are therefore postmaria, that is, postmelting, structures. Between these two classes of "white" craters there are actually many "white" craters of intermediate size. They lack the perfect regularity of the cones but are undamaged by subsequent events. Dionysius is an example, and many more may be seen on any good photograph of the full moon. In them the white substance has usually spilled somewhat outside the bounds of the crater proper, which is also intermediate between the cones and the ray craters. It is concluded that *the white craters form one continuous class,* and the ray craters show this class to be of the *postmelting era.* By contrast, heavily damaged craters—like Clavius [Plate XII] and nearly all other large craters in that region except Tycho—cannot or can barely be recognized at full moon; they are considered to belong to the premelting era. The smaller white craters can be recognized under oblique illumination not merely by their undamaged outlines but also by their greater depths.

The fact that the postmelting craters are brilliant white at full moon and the premelting craters are nearly invisible demonstrates that the texture of the crust changed drastically during the melting stage. The distribution of the "white" craters over the moon further shows that the heating and melting was a *general* phenomenon and not limited to the surface layers of the present maria, as has been supposed in the recent literature. In other words, the heat causing the melting of the maria was not primarily derived from the kinetic energy of impacts but was largely pre-existing at the time of the impacts and was due to a general heating of the moon by its own radioactivity. The interval during which maria could form was thus limited. The evidence on the relative ages of lunar structures is entirely in accord with this.

A number of subsidiary problems need further investigation. What is the nature of the white substance? Is it rock flour, known from terrestrial meteor craters, or more like pulverized glass or glass beads, as suggested by the strong back-scattering power? Why are the isolated mountain peaks in Mare Imbrium, south of Plato, covered with this substance and, indeed, the steep inside slopes of the Apennines?

The Central Peaks. Among the most puzzling lunar phenomena are the central peaks found in a fraction of the craters. Some writers have regarded them as volcanoes which deposited the crater walls, thought to consist of ashes; others, as a rebound action of the soil after the impact or even as the "stuck" planetesimal itself. Consistent with the earlier parts of this paper, only the "rebound" picture needs to be considered; but, while one can visualize a rebound in a liquid or plastic, there seems no reason to suppose that a solid can act in this manner. On the earth isostatic adjustments occur only over large areas, of the order of 1,000 kilometers in diameter and larger. With the lower gravity on the moon, such compensation could not occur in a crater, unless the impact caused local melting or fissures which tapped a large reservoir of lava farther down. Therefore, the central peaks might consist of extrusive, igneous rock; but, if so, the question would remain as to why the extrusion occurred in some craters and not in others.

In my visual observations with the 82-inch telescope I have paid much attention to the central peaks, and my general impression is that they are igneous masses, pressed up as lavas through the crater bottoms. They do not look like rubble or fractured material, as the crater walls do. Instead, they rise as majestic peaks, singly or several in a group, like simple, "functional" structures; often they have sharping sloping ridges and crests, giving the mountain an angular appearance. Often, besides impressive central mountains, one finds groups of lower, rounded mountains over a good part of the crater floor or surrounding the central peaks; they may show the flow lines of squeezed-out lava. Crater Franklin is a good example. Only very exceptionally does one find a central mountain mass that looks very different from this. The strangest case is Crater Alpetragius [Plates XIIIa, XXII], which at certain illuminations resembles a bird's nest containing two eggs, one large and one small. One might wonder whether in this case one actually sees the planetesimal. (One does occasionally find *grooves* where one can see the fragment that apparently caused it, stuck at the end of the groove.)

If the central peaks were squeezed up as lavas, this would seem to imply two things: (1) there was previously a lack of isostatic compensation or at least an excess pressure under the new crater, and (2) a lava reservoir was available. The first conclusion is consistent with a striking group of three craters near the center of the lunar disk, Ptolemy, Alphonsus, and Arzachel [Plates XII, XIIIa, XXII], which seem not very different in age; all three show damage done by flying fragments from Mare Imbrium, and, from the lack of serious damage by other impacts, they may be classed as late premelting era. Observations show that the bottom levels of these craters are very different, decreasing in level in the order in which the craters were mentioned. The central peaks vary in the opposite sense. Ptolemy has none, Alphonsus a small one, and Arzachel a huge one.

The second condition implies that craters formed in the early premelting era probably could not form central peaks, while those formed shortly before, during, and shortly after the formation of the maria could; and, again, very late postmare craters could not. This accords well with the observations. The many very early formations around Tycho and near the south pole, referred to before, have no central peaks. Conversely, craters with central peaks are, on the whole, fairly well preserved and cannot therefore, as a group, be early premelting. It is not unlikely that in marginal cases the heat of impact contributed to the availability of a lava reservoir; but the relations stated on the presence and absence of peaks indicate that the impacts were not the principal cause of the lava.

Related to this question of isostatic compensation are the craters whose bottoms have been clearly raised since their formation, some to the point of overflow. Of the latter group, Wargentin is the famous example; another case, near the center of the disk is a medium-sized crater just south of Godin. In both cases a thin old crust was apparently lifted by the upwelling lava, although a few patches of dark lava show through; this is seen at full moon. There are very many other spots on the moon where the lava apparently welled up through the crust and is now causing small and large dark patches all over the moon, except near Tycho and the south pole, where the crust has held together. A very remarkable event occurred in Crater Posidonius, where the upwelling lava apparently lifted the entire crater bottom and rammed it at a higher level sideways against the southwest crater wall, causing it to break in two and causing four parallel ridges of folded mountains to form on the old floor. The break occurred not precisely at the rim of the floor but somewhat farther out, so that the lower terrace of the wall was included. It was lifted to the level of the outer terrace. The opposite side left the lava exposed, which shows as a dark crescent around the old floor. (The unusual side motion may have occurred when Mare Imbrium formed.) These instances are but a few that could be cited, showing very clearly that the lava came from *below* and not from one or two impact areas, like Mare Imbrium. It resulted in many isolated small and larger patches of lava all over the surface of the moon. Flow from one or two central hearths would have caused systematic level differences between the lava fields, for which there is no evidence.

* The Lunar Dust

In other articles by Baldwin and Kuiper in this book, it has been either explicitly or tacitly assumed that the dark areas, called maria, on the moon are vast lava flows. There is some difference of opinion as to how the lava got there. But no one doubts it is lava. The maria certainly *look* as if they consist of a smooth flat sheet of lava. When we land on the moon, the maria should be the logical place to do it.

Then in 1955, T. Gold published a paper under the innocent title of *The Lunar Surface* which challenged some of our most cherished beliefs about the moon. For he presented reasons for believing that the maria are not lava flows at all. Instead he asserted that they are great basins filled with dust hundreds of feet deep. The dust was supposed to come from the denudation of the highlands. This is the reason the highlands are lighter than the lowlands (maria). The surface of the maria have been darkened due to long exposure from solar X rays and corpuscles. The highlands have only recently been exposed to solar radiation. How does the dust get from the highlands to the lowlands? In the absence of an atmosphere this would seem impossible to explain. But Gold proposes several transport mechanisms which he believes are quite adequate to meet the demands of his theory. Thus the maria are formed by erosion of the highlands. Erosion is one process we have always supposed was impossible on the moon. Now Gold tells us it has been going on all the time!

Astronomers are willing enough to admit a thin film of dust on the moon but they balk when it comes to admitting dust 300 feet deep. Yet the hypothesis of a deep dust layer finds considerable support from measurements of the change in temperature of the lunar surface that occurs when the light of the sun is suddenly cut off during an eclipse. At present, opinion is divided on the subject. Probably most astronomers still favor the lava flow hypothesis. There is no denying, however, that Gold has made us seriously reconsider our thinking on the subject.

*

The Lunar Surface

T. GOLD

THE *major surface features.* The most obvious fact concerning the lunar surface is that there are two different types of ground. One type is rough, covered with multiple, overlapping, circular craters and comparatively light in color. The other is darker, much smoother, and frequently so accurately level and flat as to resemble a liquid; and it possesses only a small fraction of the number-density of craters. The surface of the largest regions of flat ground—the maria—does not differ in appearance from that of smaller regions, and there is not much difficulty in classifying the surface everywhere according to these two types. We shall refer to them as "rock" and "filler." The filler is the material that has been regarded by many as solidified lava.

As has been pointed out by Baldwin and others, the craters are of shapes and configurations that would be adequately accounted for by intense explosions. Markings radiate out from some of them, the so-called rays, which can be reasonably interpreted as small debris flung out beyond the rim.

The craters, walled plains, and maria have usually been so classified according to the size of the formation. But, as is also pointed out by Baldwin, there is no real difference in type: it is a continuous distribution of objects without any clear breaks, although some features gradually change along the sequence. It is therefore undesirable to account for these objects by more than one basic process.

The classification into a time sequence. It is useful first to investigate the methods whereby it is possible to classify features according to their relative absolute time scale to be made; some dynamical considerations have been used, but they are indirect so far as detailed features are concerned, and they have to rely upon estimates of the rate of transfer of angular momentum through tidal friction in the distant past, which is necessarily rather uncertain; and they have to rely upon the moon having once possessed no stiffness and therefore having acquired the shape formerly appropriate to hydrostatic equilibrium, which the following considerations place in doubt.

T. Gold, from *Monthly Notices of the Royal Astronomical Society*, 1955, Vol. 115, No. 6.

There are various criteria for relative dating. The "criterion of overlap" is the most obvious and certain. If there are two craters that overlap each other then the one with the unbroken rim is the younger and the one whose rim was broken into the older. In the case of two craters that overlap and are of similar diameter the application of the criterion is entirely obvious. But it can also be applied in cases where one crater is very much smaller than the other, and is embedded entirely in the rim of the other. An explosion throwing up the large rim could not leave a smaller marking intact, and the small crater must hence have been formed after the large one. A large crater occurring after a small one in the same locality will lead to the total destruction of the small one, and such overlap cannot be seen except where the difference in size is not very great.

Another relative age criterion is given by the rays. As these are features which must have originated at the same time as the parent crater and which overlie the surrounding surface it is possible to say that a crater with its rays is younger than any features over which the rays can be seen. Again this is a definite criterion that cannot reasonably be questioned in the framework of the meteoritic theory. But it is of limited applicability owing to the small number of craters that possess visible rays.

The main importance of these two age criteria lies in the fact that they suggest and vindicate a third one: the sharpness of features. Crater rims and other detail vary greatly in the degree of sharpness, and it is found in all cases of overlapping groups of craters that when there is a clear difference between the members in this respect, then it is the youngest one on the criterion of overlap which shows the sharpest features. This rule can be checked with the aid of so many examples that it is not in doubt. The criterion of the rays implies in fact that the craters possessing rays are younger than any other features: the rays never appear to be in part overlapped by other features. It is therefore in agreement with the previous rule that the ray craters are also distinguished by the possession of the sharpest features.

The fact that the sharpness of features appears as an age criterion is not only of importance as a means of relative dating of formations that could not be classified by the other criteria; great interest attaches to it from the point of view of the physical processes that must for this reason be assumed to have occurred.

Instead of discussing the apparent sharpness and ruggedness of the rims of craters it is possible to include more measurable features without losing the significant correlation with the other age criteria. The height of the rim can be assumed to follow a certain law with crater diameter, as displayed by the youngest craters; the amount by which the rim of a crater is below the appropriate height can then also be taken as an indication of its age. Similarly, the loss of depth of the bowl is correlated with the other age criteria. But although the correlation of all these features with age cannot be doubted, it is clear that there is present a considerable spread for reasons other than age as well. The crater Copernicus [Plate XV], for example, which is 56 miles in diameter, has a rim only 3,300 feet high, while Tycho [Plate XII], with a diameter of 54 miles, has a rim 7,900 feet high; yet the possession of rays and the ruggedness of features and their sharpness in both cases excludes the interpretation of the difference as an age effect.

The hypothesis of erosion. The age correlation of the sharpness of features of craters could be explained in two ways: either that they were of different appearance when formed, due to a progressive change in the process of formation or in the lunar surface material; or, and this is the explanation pursued here, that a process of erosion has taken place which has resulted in gradual changes. The interpretation using a process of erosion is made attractive because all changes that have to be accounted for are in the sense of diminishing the gravitational potential energy. The absence of any clear-cut division in respect of the sharpness of features rules out any single sudden process of erosion, but implies that erosion must have been progressing through the major part of the interval of time during which the craters that are now visible were formed.

There is, however, no way of judging whether the rate of erosion has been constant or whether it has varied and perhaps diminished as the rate of bombardment diminished. Geological evidence and present-day terrestrial evidence places upper limits on the rates of bombardment sustained by the earth and by implication also by the moon. For an explanation of the lunar features it is undoubtedly necessary to suppose the rate of bombardment to have diminished very greatly since very early geological epochs. This would be in agreement with the point of view that the materials responsible for forming the bodies of the solar system have gradually been used up, leaving at the present time only a small fraction that has escaped capture. At the present time, there may still be falling onto the earth objects large enough to make a crater of the order of one mile in diameter at a mean rate of one every ten thousand years. Such small craters do not stand up for long to terrestrial erosion and we can here only see the results of the last twenty or thirty thousand years; but even this small rate would not be insignificant on the moon, where it would imply that some tens of thousands ought to be visible unless they also suffered from erosion. It is unfortunate that there seems to be no consideration available at present that allows one to derive an absolute time scale for the lunar events or to sort out to what extent the rate of erosion has been dependent on the varying rate of bombardment.

It should also be noted that there is no way of deciding how many craters may have been submerged by processes of erosion and bombardment; there is no hint that any surface is exhibited which antedates the meteoric bombardment. Thus from an examination of the surface it is not possible to place a limit on the amount of bombardment that the moon has received or on the depth of material which has been acquired by this process; and one cannot exclude the possibility that the entire moon has been built up by the same processes that are now inferred from its present surface. If indeed the moon has been put together in that way then it would not be unreasonable to think of smaller pieces having been put together earlier in the sequence of events; and therefore it would not be surprising to expect large impacts to have occurred in the process, so large that the present shape of the moon has been dictated solely by the subsequent hydrostatic adjustments which the limit of strength of the material implies and not by any statistical symmetry which would have occurred had only finely divided matter been accreted.

If a similar history were envisaged for the earth it would not follow that any of the major features here need still be attributed to the original bombardment. The earth with its denser core and its lighter continents gives every evidence of differentiation of material having occurred and of internal changes having been a dominant factor in its evolution. The growth of continents and the folding of mountain chains many times over in the geological record are processes that have certainly been absent on the moon; but on the earth these processes have undoubtedly reshaped the entire surface.

The hypothesis of erosion has been accepted by many authors, in many cases without a discussion of the implications. To be satisfied with an explanation of the loss of height and sharpness of the crater features in terms of erosion it is, however, also necessary to find the present location of all eroded material whose absence is postulated on some of the formations. We shall discuss later the possibility that the eroded material constitutes the filler, and that this fills the floors of the maria as well as some smaller craters.

The flat plains. On the material referred to as "filler" the number-density of craters is very much smaller than on the rock. With a meteoritic origin of craters, it is necessary to account for this distribution by some process that occurred after the formation of most of the craters. The filler material must have been distributed over the low ground in the characteristically flat and level manner, drowning or obliterating all existing craters in these regions and registering subsequent impacts only. Lava has usually been considered in this connection.

There are several objections to the lava flow hypothesis, which probably owed its origin to the connection with volcanism when a volcanic origin of the craters was considered probable. The most important objection is connected with the impossibility of finding a plausible time sequence for the events.

The filler fills the largest craters, the maria, as well as many others of much smaller size distributed without obvious pattern over the rest of the hemisphere.

The density of craters made in the filler material is low in all areas of filler. On the basis of the lava flow hypothesis it must therefore be supposed that lava flows occurred at about the same epoch and that this was at the stage when only a few per cent of the visible bombardment was still to come. The rims of the maria and of the craters filled with filler show, however, the highest density of small craters that occurs anywhere. It therefore could not be supposed that the process of formation of these large craters was itself responsible for letting in the lava by establishing a hole in a supposedly thin crust. The lava would have had to find its way into all those craters separately much later than they were formed. This process would have had to occur for many comparatively small craters on high ground, most of whose craters antedate the supposed floods. Although supposedly frequently punctured in the bottoms of craters, the ground never cracked to produce intrusions and outpourings of lava from fissures. Any substantial distortions of the ground could easily be recognized from the shapes of the old craters, and such distortions are conspicuously absent. There is no buckling, no overthrusting, no folding, yet old craters are frequently filled up to some level, quite often a different level in near-by but unconnected craters.

The requirement therefore would be for a very large amount of melting to have occurred on the moon in a late phase after the bulk of the bombardment was over. Melting would have to occur at such shallow depths that even comparatively small craters that had long existed on high ground would let the lava in. The lava must therefore have been within 3,000 feet or less of the surface in very many places. A large amount of hydrostatic unbalance, both due to the great height of existing crater rims and also implied by the different levels of filling, would, however, have to avoid causing any distortion of the large regions of the order of a thousand miles of connected highlands. This is not plausible. Alone, the changes of mean density associated with melting or compacting would have produced bigger effects; and the outpourings on the enormous scale and the high fluidity for the lava to run flat over very large distances cannot have left a thin skin of broken-up material undisturbed, except for many local intrusions into the bottoms of shallow depressions.

Though the connected maria have often been assumed to be the result of a single outpouring there are many craters in the outer regions of these maria that have unbroken rims standing high above the level surfaces, and that are nevertheless filled with filler. Each one of those must have been punctured from below separately. This hypothesis is clearly unsatisfactory.

The great regions of quite undisturbed highland, the absence of large volcanic structures, of foldings and large rifts or thrusts, over periods that must be comparable with or longer than the entire interval of terrestrial geology, suggests not only the absence of volcanic events, huge by terrestrial standards; but it suggests that the moon has been mechanically very much more stable than the earth and that the stability must be sought in lesser effects of heating and the attendant changes of arrangement and of density of materials. These considerations favor the view that the moon has been substantially cold throughout the period registered by any of its present surface features.

It has been suggested (Urey, 1952) that the lava could have been produced by the heat supplied in the major impacts. This suggestion also runs into the difficulty concerning the much later date of formation of the flat surfaces than of the rims surrounding them. Also, it is considered very unlikely that large quantities of liquid can result from impacts. Liquefaction would have to be due to the transport into the material of energy made available at the impact. The transport by conduction of heat cannot account for more than a very thin layer of liquefaction. However much heat is supplied externally to a piece of solid material, its surface cannot be maintained at a temperature higher than the one at which it vaporizes. (If heat is supplied at a higher temperature, then the rate of vaporization may be high and the vapor may heat up to the high temperature.) The depth below the vaporization surface to which enough heat for melting can be conducted in the brief interval of seconds during which heat is supplied in the case of an impact explosion is given by the material properties and does not exceed some centimeters for any material. If the amount of heat supplied is much in excess of that necessary to keep the surface at the vaporization temperature, then the amount of melting will be diminished, for the vaporization front will penetrate into the material, chasing the liquefaction front.

The other possible mechanism of distribution of heat is by the shock wave progressing through the material. A single pressure impulse of adequate intensity can cause melting, though special material properties are required if vaporization at the maximum pressure is to be avoided. The most favorable material for this will be one whose final density at the end of the pressure cycle is much greater than before the application of the pulse, and where consequently a large change in the internal energy is implied. Sand would be a material of this type. Whether the heating resulting from a single pressure pulse can ever be large in a material whose final density is similar to the initial one is uncertain; the energy available there can only correspond to the area between the two curves of the pressure-volume diagram, whose end points are common. The effect depends upon the material possessing very much hysteresis in the pressure-density relation. It is possible, of course, that pressure-induced phase changes may show substantial hysteresis of this sort.

In the case of an explosion, the sound wave radiating into the material suffers geometrical attenuation so that the energy density diminishes as the inverse square of the distance from the focus, augmented by the high physical attenuation implied by the intended melting. The energy density must therefore diminish rapidly from the focus, and the heating would be expected to diminish even more rapidly. This will restrict the volume in which the heating is adequate to melt and inadequate to vaporize. It is to be expected that in practice most of the energy will go into making a very hot vapor, and most of the remainder into fracturing and pulverizing the solid, but very little into melting, a process that requires too high a degree of uniformity in the conditions and too small a range of temperatures at which heat has to be supplied.

In connection with the lava flow hypothesis, the view has been advanced that the darker color of the maria compared with the high ground is simply the consequence of the lava being a darker material than the other type of rock. This view leads to insuperable difficulties. If erosion is assumed to be the cause of the rounding of the features of old craters, as discussed earlier, then it is necessary to find the eroded material. This cannot reasonably be expected to have all left the moon entirely. If an estimate is made of the amounts missing from the rims of all the many overlapping old craters, then this cannot come to less than the equivalent of a 300-foot depth if it were distributed over the entire surface, and probably a good deal more. Though on the lava flow hypothesis it could be supposed that the eroded material was so distributed that it was all drowned, the question would remain as to the whereabouts of the material eroded after the supposed lava flooding. This is still a substantial depth, at any rate deeper by a large factor than is necessary to make it optically opaque. Even if the erosion process were not to take the erosion product any farther than is strictly required by the change of shapes, there would still have to be large areas of the flat plains covered over by that material. This is clearest in the cases of flat-bottomed craters whose erosion on the inner crater walls must be assumed to have covered over at least part of the flat bottom, yet the color there even close to the sharp edge is the same as that of the flat surfaces elsewhere. A more diffuse distribution of the eroded material would only strengthen this argument, so it must be concluded that the darker shade is that of eroded material even if it came from lighter rock.

The disappearance of rays demands a similar explanation. If older craters also produced rays as the most recent ones have done, and as must indeed be expected, then the combined ray material would entirely cover all the surface with much more than optical thickness. On the high ground the occurrence of erosion will itself account for the removal of the ray material, but what has happened to all the rays that ought to be on the flat ground due to craters subsequent to the supposed lava flows? There are quite enough of those to have covered over the majority of the areas of the maria. All this material must either have changed its color and become darker or been covered over with eroded material from elsewhere which must in any case be presumed to be dark. In no case could the original lava surface be the one that is visible at present.

It may also be presumed that in the so-called postlava period when still a few per cent of the bombardment came, this would have been associated with enough dust to cover over the entire surface opaquely. Indeed, the estimates of dust at present still being acquired by the earth (and moon) would assure such a cover in a comparatively short time. Petterson and Rotschi (1952) estimate from the nickel content of deep ocean deposits that the quantity of material currently deposited on the earth is of the order of one million tons per year. This estimate would imply that the moon is acquiring a layer one centimeter in thickness every ten million years, at the present time. As this contribution is in the form of a very fine powder the individual impacts cannot cause any disturbance at a depth greater than about one millimeter, and except for areas of larger impacts there can be no significant mixing of materials with those at greater depths. Therefore, an opaque blanket would be spread over the entire surface, and renewed once every million years. (This consideration would be invalidated if in each little impact an amount of vapor was freed and allowed to escape from the moon entirely, of a mass of the same order as or exceeding that of the micrometeorite; or if a fraction escaped the period would be lengthened. The material making up the rays of craters would have to be at least some centimeters thick if it is not to be covered over in too short a time to account for the absence of similar craters on the earth. Until the rays are submerged they would have to be able to shed dust just like the highlands.) A process of migration of dust from high ground to the lowlands can again be invoked to account for denudation of the high ground and for that reason for a differentiation in color. Again the actual surface in the flat regions would have to be dust, and nothing is gained by supposing lava to have been darker than rock.

If erosion has been continuous, then it is necessary to suppose the present ray craters to be very young compared with the age of the great majority of the features. This will no doubt mean that they occurred in the time covered by geology on the earth, while most of the other features can be considered older than the available geological record. A few similar stragglers hitting the earth within the last hundred million years may well be expected to have their markings obscured by the vigorous processes on the earth's surface, which must of course also be expected to have entirely obliterated a multitude of lunar type craters in perhaps three thousand million years.

The ray craters need not be so young if the processes of erosion and changes of color of the surface were dependent upon the infalling material. In that case the great diminution of the bombardment which must in any case be inferred will have implied a similar diminution in the rate of erosion, and the last craters to have been formed must be uneroded.

The amounts of eroded material missing on the high ground are large, and the absence of any signs of this material on the filler, especially around the sharp edges of maria, or the sharp junction between crater walls and flat surfaces, requires in any case a special hypothesis, whatever origin of the flat surfaces is assumed. It is necessary to suppose that the eroded material distributes itself over the flat surfaces. This supposition disposes at once of the difficulty concerning the disappearance of rays on the flat ground. These very thin markings would merely be covered over. If, then, it is necessary to suppose that a mechanism exists that allows the eroded material, presumably very fine dust, to "flow" like a fluid, then it is no longer necessary to invoke any other fluid ever to have been present to cause the flat regions. We shall pursue therefore the consequences and requirements implied by the hypothesis that all the flat regions are beds of dust whose origin lies in the erosion of the high ground as well as perhaps in newly acquired meteoric material.

The flow of dust. The smallness of the gradients in most of the sediment and the sharp distinction between the eroding rock and the sediment suggests that the flat distribution must not be the process that limits the speed of the erosion. The requirement is for the transport of dust particles to the minimum height that they can reach to occur at a rapid rate compared with the other processes of the formation or freeing of dust at the surface or its acquisition from outside. Compared with terrestrial standards the transport requirements are, of course, extremely slow: fine dust particles on the surface must be removed only at such a speed that the maria can be filled to an average depth of perhaps a thousand feet in a period that may be three thousand million years; one millimeter in ten thousand years.

The requirement is for the average speed of flow not to diminish appreciably with the angle of the slope until a very small angle is reached. It should not be a flow restricted by the equivalent of viscosity in a liquid, for this would leave slight gradients persisting for long and remove steep gradients very quickly. The type of flow required would be one where at any instant a thin layer on the surface behaves like a nonviscous liquid while the remainder underneath remains stiff. This would then allow steep slopes to persist but would assure that the deposits of dust possess a flat surface. Such a "fluidization" of a surface layer would have to be a process resulting from an external energy source, providing an agitation for the dust particles on or near the surface.

There appear to be some very steep slopes in the filler material. In particular, there are the small rills which possess very steep sides. This is not contrary to the known behavior of dust. At a depth of more than a few meters the compaction under the overlying weight would suffice to convert the material effectively into a solid; in the absence of an atmosphere, grains stick together with intermolecular forces with even less compaction than is necessary when atmospheric molecules intervene. If the material can be regarded as resistant to internal flow but possessing a thin fluidized surface layer, then the filling up of steep holes or gaps would proceed at a speed limited by the fluidization process, but the steep sides would persist until the filling up is complete. It is not a requirement that such rills should survive for a great length of time; Baldwin speaks of them as the youngest features on the moon, yet has to add that some appear partly "filled with lava." These rills are to be thought of within the framework of the present interpretations as the small signs of the small isostatic adjustments that keep occurring as the maria fill up with dust and the highlands are denuded; and these rills are in turn comparatively quickly filled in. Their distribution mainly around the edges of the great maria is entirely in accord with this interpretation.

The fluidization process remains to be discussed. It would, of course, require to be discussed in any other interpretation of the lunar surface, provided that the worn appearance of the old craters is attributed to erosion; the only difference here is that the process needs to be effective enough not only to transport the minimum amount of material that is certainly known to have been *removed*, but the somewhat larger amounts that may have been removed or acquired from outside and which are certainly known to have *accumulated*. But in no other way is the requirement changed, not even in the degree of flatness of the end result of the process.

The correct choice of the physical process responsible for the fluidization is a matter of the greatest difficulty; but it is not difficult to suggest processes that may be responsible and for which it cannot be said that they must fall short of the requirements. Perhaps the most serious consideration should be given to the effect of an evaporation and condensation cycle of a suitable vapor, to the effects of micrometeorites, and to the effects of electrostatic forces. There may be several other possible processes. Much dust may have been moved by the gas produced in the largest impacts; a flat deposition is, however, not to be expected from a few violent jerks, but only from statistical effects of a process in which each particle was lifted up many times.

An evaporation reaction is exerted on a solid particle when a volatile material is vaporized from its surface. This force arises if vapor has condensed onto the particle and then is removed again, such as by the action of sunlight heating the particle. The order of magnitude of the effect is such that the condensed material has to be about one thousandth part of the mass of a dust grain in order that the grain may be lifted by 1 cm. in fortunate circumstances. But a much more effective process may be occurring. A substance of such a molecular weight as to remain bound to the moon in the vapor phase (molecular weight more than about 50) may condense in the shade and evaporate in the sunlight. Assuming a very small atmosphere on the moon only, the substance would remain concentrated near the morning edge; it would evaporate from the material moved into the sunlight and much of it would recondense in the near-by dark regions. The remainder would distribute itself over the sunlit hemisphere but would again be caught as soon as it moved into the dark hemisphere. A given quantity of vapor would be effective many times in one lunar day if the average distance of the condensation from the region of dawn is small. (The details of the process would depend very much upon the amounts of other gases present, but for the present purposes only in such a way as to effect the quantities required for the dust transport mechanism.) Before condensing, the vapor may be expected to sink into the interstices between the dust particles and when the region becomes heated the substance will be vaporized and driven out. This may be quite enough to agitate the layer into which diffusion has occurred, a layer of perhaps a few millimeters or a centimeter in thickness.

Another source of agitation of the surface is due to all the small meteoric dust particles that must be expected to strike. This mechanism would be inadequate at the present rate of bombardment, but the entire meteoritic theory would also be inadequate at that rate. A very much higher rate has to be supposed for the past and it is then not certain that all the small explosions due to particles in the range of 0.01 to 0.0001 cm., with the puff of very hot gas generated in each one, cannot together have moved the surface dust. If the quantity of meteoric dust accumulated is thought of as being of the same order as the eroded dust, then such a method of transport is very likely. The process would satisfy the requirement of effectively fluidizing a surface layer only.

Electrical forces are also a possibility. These can arise either as a consequence of photoemission of electrons from the surface due to the ultraviolet light of the sun, or they could arise in some larger electrical process connected with solar events of the type that cause the aurorae and magnetic storms on the earth. The process of photoemission in the absence of an atmosphere, and especially of moisture, will result in an erratic distribution of charge on the irradiated surface which may be a very good insulator. While the average positive charge will be inadequate to lift particles off, it is not clear that the chance distribution in small localities could not do it. (This type of mechanism could best be investigated experimentally.) If particles were frequently dislodged by such electrostatic forces, then again a net flow would result on the surface in accordance with the requirement.

The patterns of current induced in the moon by the passage of a solar corpuscular stream have not been investigated. In the shadow zone, the conductivity of space would be very low and therefore electrostatic forces may be of importance. Effects of this type may do more than merely fluidize the surface; they may actually have the tendency to lift up and scatter any dust above a level surface, thereby speeding the establishment of level surfaces.

If very small dust particles are the rule, then their thermal agitation may be adequate to cause transportation. Professor P. Morrison has suggested (privately) that such thermal agitation can be considered as resulting in an "atmosphere" whose molecules are the dust particles. On account of the large "molecular weight" the scale height would be very small. Such an atmosphere would have just the required properties; it would move down even very slight gradients and would settle material in flat level surfaces if more material was made available from higher ground.

If the moon ever possessed an atmosphere, then the transport of dust could of course just be ascribed to wind erosion. On the whole, the appearance does not favor that interpretation, for there are no large-scale patterns and preferential directions of drifts to be discerned, while those would be expected from an atmosphere that derived its convective motion permanently from the temperature difference between the light and dark hemispheres.

The generation of dust. A process of erosion generally consists of the two stages of the breakup of the material and of its transportation. We have so far considered only the one of transportation, and this may indeed be all that is necessary. The material of the lunar surface may be composed of loose aggregate with a large proportion of dust, especially if it has always been cold and if no substantial processes have been present to deliver compacted or fused material to the surface. All the impacts that are indicated would have generated much fine powder, and even if more substantial pieces are present in the crater walls they may be so embedded in dust that the removal of the dust would make them tumble.

It is, however, possible to suggest processes that would cause more dust to be formed from solid rock provided it is quickly removed and does not protect the surface. The solar radiation in the region of ultraviolet and soft X rays will be absorbed on the lunar surface and may cause there a destruction of a thin surface layer. It must be remembered that all the radiation which is responsible on the earth for the heating and ionization of the outer atmosphere will there be absorbed in a layer probably less than 1 mm. in thickness. Equilibrium between the resulting crystallographic destruction and the spontaneous recrystallization of the material may occur only when a large proportion of fine powder has been formed. In addition, there is the possibility of escape from the surface of certain constituents of the crystals. Oxygen, for example, could be released through the irradiation and the remaining material may not recrystallize. Even if the same material had formed into crystalline particles at a similar distance from the sun it is not necessary to suppose that those would be stable when later exposed on the lunar surface where the temperature reaches much higher values. The rates of such surface destruction required on the moon to be of significance are only of the order of 1 km. in 1,000 million years or 0.0001 cm. per year. There may also be a comparable destruction of the surface by fast impinging gas molecules in a manner very similar to the destruction of cathodes of vacuum tubes by positive ion bombardment. Lastly, micrometeorites could be held responsible not only for the supply of new dust, but also for the generation of dust from existing solids. Thus, there is no difficulty in supposing an adequate supply of dust to be present. Possibly the initial freeing of dust particles may be a restricting factor in the erosion process if the particles are at first more tightly packed than they are once they have been moved.

The darker color of the beds of sediment has to be explained. As mentioned earlier, the explanation has to be found in any case, whatever theory of the surface features is adopted, so long as erosion plays a part. It is necessary to suppose that dust which has been on the surface for a certain length of time becomes dark; this might be merely due to its mixing with fresh meteoric material. But a more complicated behavior is required. Even small craters in the maria show a lighter color and it must therefore in any case be supposed that the dark color is confined to a thin surface layer. Unless the color of recent meteoric dust is different from the older variety, one has to suppose that some chemical action takes place which alters the color of dust under the surface back to the lighter shade. Again the required rates are very low.

Another possibility would be that the darker color is produced by the action of the solar X rays on material that has been on the surface for a comparatively long time, while the denuded highlands keep presenting material that has until recently been protected. Such radiation-induced coloration is generally lost by heating, and this would explain why the fine powder that has been involved in an explosion is again turned to the lighter shade.

Comparison of highland craters with those placed in maria. The comparison of the heights of the two "recent" craters, Copernicus and Tycho, has been mentioned. The much smaller height of the rim of Copernicus may be attributed to the fact that this crater was formed entirely in dust, and that dust may behave very differently from more compacted or rocky material in the explosion. There is also a very striking difference in the appearance of the rays of those two craters. Tycho's rays are very long and straight, while those of Copernicus are much shorter and fuzzy, and a much larger area near the crater has been covered with ray material. Again, this may be an indication of the difference of the mechanical properties of the substance composing these rays.

A detailed survey of the smaller craters would be valuable, in order to establish whether the relations between diameter, depth, and height of rim are consistently different in the two types of ground. Restricting attention to ray craters will assure that the results are not confused by an unknown amount of erosion.

Conclusion. The present views are incomplete in the sense that many processes that may be concerned require further investigation. But the principal aim has been to show that there is no real requirement for the hypothesis of lava flow and to indicate the processes that may be expected to be occurring. If some of those processes are not readily susceptible to theoretical or observational investigation, this provides no argument for leaving them out of consideration.

It would be extremely difficult to investigate the details of any one of the terrestrial erosion processes in a theoretical manner if it had not been seen in fine detail; but not nearly so difficult, once the conditions on the planet are known, to suggest major agencies for the erosion process.

The views are also incomplete in the sense that there are many features that have been reported on the lunar surface for which still no explanation has been offered. But they are not the common widespread features. There is no doubt that much fine detail must remain unexplained for much longer. One must expect that of the vast amount of fine detail that can be seen, only the commonly recurring features will fit into a simple theory; that many of the rare features will reflect events of a degree of improbability that puts them well outside the useful range of speculation. There are chance effects of grazing angles of incidence of meteorites, or of tight clustering of meteorites resulting from a large piece broken up by a close passage to the earth, which may have occurred a few times, but not often enough to establish a recognizable class of features. The apparent inexplicability of such rare markings should not be used as an observational test of a theory.

* A Volcano on the Moon?

Evidences for changes on the moon have been reported occasionally, but they have all involved visual observations of a questionable nature which have failed to carry conviction. Until recently nobody has ever come forward with photographic evidence of any sort of change on the moon. This is understandable when it is remembered that very few astronomers with photographic equipment have studied the moon. Most observations of the moon have been made by devoted amateurs working with small telescopes. To catch a change on the moon by photography it is necessary either (1) to take a long series of systematic exposures of the moon; or else (2) be very lucky. At the risk of writing a foreword that is longer than the article itself, it may be worth-while to discuss fully some work that has been done on the moon since 1958, as there is so much interest in the subject.

As related in the following article, the first photographic evidence for a change on the moon was obtained on November 3, 1958, by N. A. Kozyrev of the Crimean Astrophysical Observatory. Kozyrev's observation would appear to fall in the second category. He was lucky enough to be looking at the moon as well as photographing it just when something was happening. This "something" Kozyrev describes as a "volcanic process" over the central peak of the crater Alphonsus. In justice to Kozyrev it should be said that he was deliberately looking for the kind of effect he observed, so that it was not entirely a matter of accident. What he was doing was taking a spectrogram of Alphonsus with the slit of the spectrograph across the central peak [Plates XIIIa, XIVa]. While photographing he was also observing the crater through the guiding eyepiece. At 1 hour Universal Time on the night of November 2-3, the central peak became strongly washed out and of an unusual reddish hue. After taking this spectrogram, he switched the telescope to Mars and did not get back to Alphonsus again until two hours later. At that time, he was struck by the unusual brightness and whiteness of the central peak. During a 30-minute exposure on the peak, its brightness suddenly fell to its normal value.

Here we should probably give a brief explanation of what is meant by the spectrum of a heavenly body or readers unfamiliar with this subject will not be clear on what we are talking about. Isaac Newton, in 1666 when twenty-three years old, was the first person to produce a spectrum. He did this by admitting a beam of sunlight into his darkened room through a hole in the shutter of the window. This beam, after passing through a triangular piece of glass or prism, was spread out upon the opposite wall in a colored strip. Newton noticed that the white beam of light was bent, or refracted, after passing through the prism, the violet rays the most and the red rays the least. The rainbow-colored strip apparently consisted of colored images of the hole in the shutter. Newton later succeeded in obtaining a purer series of colors by using a slit instead of a round hole, thus reducing the effect of overlapping colors. By inserting a lens between the prism and screen he was able to focus the colors sharply on the wall, in this way producing a true spectrum. This crude apparatus was the first spectroscope, or instrument for analyzing light into its separate components. Today the spectroscope is used in astronomy entirely as a *spectrograph,* since all the observations are recorded by photography. The light from a star or other object is collected by a telescope and the narrow beam is sent through the spectrograph onto a photographic plate.

Self-luminous bodies may give at least three kinds of spectra: continuous, line, absorption. Let us consider each in turn.

A luminous solid, liquid, or gas under high pressure, gives a *continuous spectrum.* That is, the spectrum consists simply of a rainbow-colored band which is continuous and unbroken from the violet at one end, to the red at the other. The glowing filament from an electric lamp gives a continuous spectrum.

A glowing gas gives a spectrum consisting of isolated bright *lines* which are simply monochromatic images of the slit. Some glowing vapors, instead of producing separate lines, give a spectrum consisting of long series of bright lines closely packed together called bands. The lines in a band are mostly closely packed together at its head which is usually sharply marked. As the lines recede from the head of a band they grow weaker and are spread farther apart. If the lines recede from the band head toward the violet, the band is said to be degraded toward the violet, or vice versa. A *line spectrum* is produced by the individual atoms of an element. A *band spectrum* is produced by molecules consisting of two or more atoms closely bound together. The head of a band forms a convenient point of reference in specifying the position of these series of lines.

The position of a line among the colors of the spectrum depends upon the wave length of the light emitted by the atoms producing it. It is difficult to measure the absolute wave length of a line, but once the wave lengths of a few fundamental lines throughout the spectrum have been determined, it is easy to find the wave lengths of other lines between them by interpolation. The wave length of spectrum lines is measured in angstrom units, named in honor of a pioneer Swedish spectroscopist. One angstrom unit, written simply "A," is 10^{-10} meters or 250 millionths of an inch. Red light has a wave length of about 6,500A; yellow light about 6,000A; green light about 5,100A; blue light about 4,500A; and violet light about 4,100A. These are the kinds of light that we can *see*. Actually the spectrum extends far beyond the violet and red into the ultraviolet and the infrared regions to which our eyes are not sensitive. We can easily explore the ultraviolet and infrared regions, however, by the use of suitably sensitive photographic plates, or other radiation sensitive instruments.

If the rainbow band formed by sunlight passing through a spectroscope is examined closely, one finds that it is not really continuous as it appears to be from casual inspection. Instead, it is found to be crossed by numerous dark lines of various degrees of intensity. Newton would have made a capital discovery if he had detected these lines, but evidently his spectroscope was too crude to show them. They were not seen again until 1802 by Wollaston, who utterly failed to appreciate their significance. In 1814, the dark lines in the solar spectrum were carefully studied and their positions recorded by the German optician Joseph Fraunhofer. In his honor, these lines are still known as Fraunhofer lines.

Experiments beginning about the middle of the nineteenth century revealed that many of the dark Fraunhofer lines occurred at the same position in the spectrum as the bright lines of different elements produced in laboratory spectra. An element in the gaseous state, in other words, seemed to absorb the identical wave lengths of light that it emitted when it was heated to incandescence. Glowing sodium vapor from common table salt, for example, produces two strong lines in the yellow which are matched exactly by two strong Fraunhofer lines in the solar spectrum. The glowing vapor of the iron arc produces hundreds of bright lines which match with Fraunhofer lines. Such close coincidence can hardly be the result of chance. The inference is strong that the dark lines in the solar spectrum are produced by the same atoms as the bright lines in the laboratory whose origin we know. In this way sixty-six of the ninety-two naturally occurring elements on earth have been identified in the sun. Often identification is based upon coincidence between scores or dozens of lines in the sun and laboratory. Since there are thousands of Fraunhofer lines, many will match closely with laboratory lines purely by chance. If some of the weaker Fraunhofer lines of an element match with laboratory lines but the stronger ones do not, then we know the coincidence must be accidental. The presence of some of the rare elements in the sun depends upon coincidence with only one or two of their strongest lines. In such cases only an expert can decide whether an element is probably present in the sun or not.

Most of the stars give spectra which are continuous except where they are crossed by dark lines. Stars hotter than the sun show only a few dark lines; stars cooler than the sun show many more. The cool red stars have long portions of their spectra blotted out by molecular bands. A few exceptional stars show bright lines.

The dark lines arise from *absorption* of light in the cooler atmosphere of a star overlying the hotter surface below. A spectrum roughly simulating that of a star can be produced in the laboratory. Let light from the intensely hot filament of an electric lamp shine through the cooler vapor of glowing sodium. We get a continuous spectrum from the filament of the lamp except where it is crossed by two dark lines due to absorption by the sodium vapor. If the current through the lamp is decreased until the sodium vapor is brighter than the filament, we will get two bright yellow lines superimposed upon a weak continuous spectrum. The presence of dark and bright lines in the spectrum of a star follows from similar considerations, although a detailed discussion of the processes involved may be extremely complex.

Now we can proceed to the description of Kozyrev's spectrum observations of the moon.

Kozyrev relates that he did not give any serious thought to his visual observations of Alphonsus, believing them merely to involve changes due to the quality of the seeing. But upon developing his plates, he found that the second one taken from 3:00 to 3:30 showed a series of bright emission bands superimposed on the usual solar spectrum of the central peak. He believes that what happened was that first there was an ejection of dust or volcanic ash which appeared red in the guiding eyepiece, followed by an efflux of gases that produced the emission spectrum.

The most interesting feature photographed is a bright band degraded toward the violet with its head at 4,737 angstroms that appears on the spectrogram taken at 3:00 to 3:30. This is at the position of one of the strongest bands in the so-called Swan spectrum of carbon produced by the C_2 molecule. (It is called the Swan spectrum because years ago these bands were observed in the candle flame by a physicist named Swan.) Kozyrev considers that the identification with C_2 is confirmed by the presence of two other of the Swan bands with heads at 5,165 and 5,635A, which he says appear weakly, although they cannot be seen on the reproduction of the spectra.

G. P. Kuiper of the Yerkes Observatory has criticized Kozyrev's identification of the 4,737 feature with C_2 on the ground that the photographic copies fail to show any band lines or band structure but only a continuous emission streak overlying the solar spectrum. Also, he believes that against the sunlit moon, the 4,737 Swan band should show in absorption rather than emission. The associated band at 5,129A should be weakly present in emission. This follows from the classification of the relevant vibrational states and the known transition probabilities. In the ordinary Swan spectrum the band at 5,165A is the strongest, whereas it is very weak or absent in the spectrum taken by Kozyrev. Kuiper believes that the identification of the feature beginning at 4,737A is unknown, and that it cannot be due to C_2, whose presence would hardly be expected on the basis of terrestrial experience.

To this Kozyrev has replied that while the structure of the emission band is inconspicuous on the photograph it does show up on his microphotometer tracings of the original plate. (It should be pointed out that the lines in the Swan bands are very closely packed together so it is perhaps not surprising that they fail to show individually on a low dispersion spectrogram.) Undoubtedly other bands of unknown origin are superimposed on the Swan bands. As to whether the bands should appear in emission or absorption, Kozyrev emphasizes that at such very low densities molecular collisions cannot play any role. Therefore, all processes of radiation transfer will be of the pure scattering type, without true absorption such as occurs in the dense atmospheres of Jupiter and Saturn. In the highly rarified lunar atmosphere the gas illuminated by the sun must give emission and not absorption bands. The shining of the gases is produced in the same way as the luminescence of a comet.

About six months after Kozyrev's account of his observations appeared, two amateurs in San Diego published a paper entitled "Recent Observations of Possible Volcanic Activity within the Lunar Crater Alphonsus."* These observers were H. F. Poppendiek of the Physics Section and W. H. Bond of the Thermodynamic Section of Convair. Their observations were made with a Newtonian reflector of 6 inches aperture and 52 inches focal length. Poppendiek had been observing the moon and planets for twenty years, his principal interest being the moon.

On the evening of November 18, 1958, at about 8 P. M., Pacific Standard Time (PST), they were startled by what they saw within the crater Alphonsus. A large diffuse cloud completely obscured the crater's central peak and its small craterlet. The cloud was about 20 miles in diameter and irregular in shape, its general appearance being as depicted in the drawing reproduced in Plate XIIIb. Two main features attracted their attention: (1) the cloud was large in comparison to the peak that it obscured, and (2) it had a strange diffuse brightness. Alphonsus was near the terminator at the time, the dividing line between daylight and darkness on the moon. Ordinarily when looking at features near the terminator, one sees mainly strongly contrasting black and white areas. In this case, however, they observed not only the extremely bright white walls of the crater illuminated by the sun and the black shadow on the crater floor, but also a grayish, diffuse cloud whose brightness was somewhere between the two extremes. The side of the cloud toward the sun was not noticeably brighter than the other. They watched the cloud for 20 to 30 minutes, alternately looking at the moon and Mars. During this period they saw no change in its size or shape.

They scrutinized Alphonsus again a month later when the moon was at the same phase. This time there was no diffuse cloud and the central peak with its craterlet was visible. A comparison of surface details around Alphonsus with older photographs failed to show any significant differences in topography.

After reading about Kozyrev's observation of a bright cloud over the central

---

* *Publications of the Astronomical Society of the Pacific*, June, 1959, p. 233.

peak of Alphonsus, Poppendiek and Bond decided maybe they should say something about their own observations. Accordingly on December 14 in the San Diego *Union,* they publicly announced their observations of November 18. When asked why they had waited so long before making their announcement, they replied they had held back for fear of ridicule. Almost every textbook in astronomy asserts that the moon is a dead world, and as amateurs they hesitated to state that they had seen activity on the moon. Kozyrev's results, however, made their own observations seem more credible.

The observations of Alphonsus on November 18 by Poppendiek and Bond would seem to be strong confirmation of Kozyrev's findings of November 3. Unfortunately it is not that simple. It happened that Walter H. Haas,* an experienced amateur planetary observer, was also looking at Alphonsus on the evening of November 18, from 7:20 P. M. to 9:20 P. M., PST, using a 12½-inch reflector with a magnification of 303X. At 7:20, little showed in Alphonsus but the central peak, but by 9:20 about two thirds of the floor was in sunlight. Haas did not watch continuously but was never away from the telescope for more than 20 to 25 minutes at a time. He reports that everything about Alphonsus seemed completely normal and ordinary, including the central peak. If the time given by Poppendiek and Bond of 8^h PST is correct, then Haas says his observations contradict theirs. He believes that he could not have overlooked anything as gross as they describe.

Thus, considerable doubt is thrown on these later observations. Under the circumstances, we cannot put much faith in the observations of Poppendiek and Bond as they are not confirmed by an experienced observer working with a larger telescope. As for Kozyrev's observations, one of his spectra does show an unmistakable emission feature beginning at 4,737A which is not on his other exposures. This emission band appears to be real, indicating that some sort of gaseous outburst actually did occur over the central peak in Alphonsus. Whether the emission was produced by the C_2 molecule or not is another problem. It will probably be a long time before we get additional evidence on this point as an observer has to be extremely lucky to be ready to photograph just when a rare event is happening on the moon. But since Alphonsus will undoubtedly be a target for telescopes now, there is some hope that the situation may be clarified in the near future. Kozyrev's account is fairly technical at times but the importance of its subject merits its inclusion here.

* *Publications of the Astronomical Society of the Pacific,* June, 1959, p. 236.

✳

Observations of a Volcanic Process on the Moon

NIKOLAI A. KOZYREV

FOR many years in the past, observers have reported possible changes on the moon's surface. Especially interesting among such reports are those of the appearance of haze that veiled details of the lunar craters. These visual observations, however, remained unconfirmed, since the visibility of such details depends strongly on the angle of illumination by the sun and possibly on the quality of the atmospheric seeing.

More objective evidence for such haze was obtained in October, 1956, by Dinsmore Alter, on a series of photographs of the craters Ptolemaeus, Alphonsus, and Arzachel, in blue and infrared light. He used the 60-inch reflector of Mount Wilson Observatory.

This part of the lunar surface, located near the center of the disk, is very interesting because it contains a number of parallel fissures, which presumably came into existence after the formation of the craters. Due to the diffusion of light by the earth's atmosphere, all photographs in blue light have considerably less contrast than infrared ones. But the details on the floor of the crater Alphonsus appeared particularly washed out in Dr. Alter's photographs in blue light. I became convinced that this effect deserved serious attention and that on the floor of that crater there might occur an effusion of gases.

It should be understood at the outset that the washing-out effect cannot be caused by the diffusion of light in such gases on the moon. For this to occur, the layer would require a total density like that of the earth's atmosphere, that is, of the order of 10^{25} molecules per square centimeter of surface. But if the gases can be made fluorescent under the action of strong short-wave (hard) solar radiation, then for veiling to occur the gas need only absorb all such hard radiation of the sun. The coefficient of absorption will be very large for corpuscular, X-ray, and extreme ultraviolet solar energy.

Therefore, we might suppose that a layer of gas of the order of 10^{15} molecules per square centimeter—about 10^{-10} atmosphere—would have considerable

Nikolai A. Kozyrev, from *Sky and Telescope,* February, 1959.

fluorescence. The existence of such a localized "atmosphere" due to the effusion of gases from lunar craters seems entirely possible.

The question remains of whether the sun's short-wave energy is intense enough to produce fluorescent radiation in the visible part of the spectrum that could be seen against the background of the ordinary solar spectrum reflected by the moon. Incidentally, it should be noted that the Czech astronomer F. Link has argued in favor of fluorescence by minerals located on the surface of the moon.

Using spectral methods in 1955, I obtained some direct evidence for the existence of fluorescence in the ray system of the bright crater Aristarchus, reaching in violet light about 15 per cent of the ordinary reflected lunar light. This result, obtained by comparing the contours of the Fraunhofer lines of the solar spectrum and the reflected lunar spectrum, showed that it would be possible to attempt observing gas effusions on lunar crater floors.

In October and November, 1958, together with V. I. Ezerski of the Kharkov Observatory, I was conducting spectral investigations of Mars, using the 50-inch reflector of the Crimean Observatory of the Academy of Sciences of the Soviet Union. At that same time, I decided to obtain systematically some photometrically standardized spectrograms of lunar details, in particular of the crater Alphonsus.

During these observations, the slit of the spectrograph was always oriented east-west on the sky. The linear dispersion was 23A per millimeter in the vicinity of the hydrogen-gamma line, and the scale of lunar details about 10 seconds of arc per millimeter. The normal exposure on Kodak 103a-F emulsion was 10 to 30 minutes.

Nothing special was noticed on the spectrograms of Alphonsus up to the night of November 2-3, when three spectrograms were taken with the slit running through its central peak, as shown in the picture [Plate XIIIa]. While I was taking the first spectrogram, at 1ʰ Universal Time, and guiding on the image of the central peak, the latter became strongly washed out and of an unusual reddish hue.

After taking this spectrogram, however, and in accordance with our program, we changed over to observe Mars, and the next spectrogram of Alphonsus was made from 3:00 to 3:30 Universal time, a 30-minute exposure. Only the central peak of this crater showed on the slit, and I was struck by its unusual brightness and whiteness at the time.

During the exposure, I did not take my eye away from the guiding eyepiece, but suddenly I noticed that the brightness of the peak had fallen to its normal value. The spectrogram exposure was then immediately stopped and the following one was taken, from 3:30 to 3:40, with the same position of the slit.

I did not give serious thought to my vivid impressions, believing that all the peculiarities I had noticed were caused by a change in the quality of the observing conditions. Therefore, it came somewhat as a surprise when development of the spectrograms showed that all the changes noted visually had in reality occurred on the central peak of Alphonsus.

On the first spectrogram, the central peak is considerably weakened in violet light compared with the neighboring details of the crater [see letter at end of article], a fact that was not observed on earlier spectra. Measurement of this photograph showed that the absorption varied inversely with the wave length, and the calculated general absorption turned out to be equal to 15 or 20 per cent in the visual region.

On the second spectrogram this absorption is not noticeable, and an emission spectrum stands out, composed of a series of broad bands superimposed on the usual spectrum of the central peak. The second spectrogram taken with a 10-minute exposure immediately afterward shows only the normal appearance of the crater. Therefore, the phenomenon of gas effusion lasted not longer than two and one-half hours and not less than half an hour.

On the following night, November 3-4, I obtained two more spectra of Alphonsus, but its condition continued to be normal. Then the moon entered the last quarter phase and this region of its surface was in shadow and unobservable.

These observations are interpreted as showing that on the morning of November 3, 1958, there occurred a volcanic phenomenon. First there was an ejection of dust—volcanic ash (appearing reddish in the guiding eyepiece) — and afterward an efflux of gas (causing the emission spectrum). The effusion of gas could come from magma rising to the lunar surface.

The most noticeable peculiarity of the emission spectrum of the central peak is the group of bands starting at 4,737A, sharply delimited on the long-wave side. These bands have 40 per cent of the normal luminosity of the peak in these wave lengths. But the emission is not superimposed directly on the peak, being slightly shifted away from the shadow, that is, toward the sun. This shift amounts to approximately 0.7 seconds of arc, or about 1½km. on the moon's surface. It can probably be explained by the sun's short-wave radiation penetrating only those parts of the gaseous layer that were nearest the sun.

One must presume that the shining of these gases was produced similarly to the luminescence of a comet, the solar radiation causing dissociation of the complex original molecules issuing from beneath the surface. Optically active molecular radicals were produced, which fogged the observable spectrum for a time. Such an effect could not, of course, occur on the dark side of the moon.

Photometric measurements of the spectrogram also indicate that the shadow of the central peak in the region of the bright bands is somewhat deeper than in other places along the spectrum outside these bands. From this, we can conclude that the optical depth of the gases in the observed emission was greater than unity and that the dimensions of the gaseous layer were not much smaller than those of the central peak, whose height is approximately 1.3 km.

To obtain a full interpretation of the emission spectrum, it is necessary to analyze its intensity carefully, subtracting step by step from its observed intensity at each wave length the intensity of the neighboring part of the crater bottom. Such measurements require great precision and are not yet finished. But some information has already been obtained.

In the strong group of bands that start at 4,737A, progressively weakening toward the violet, there appears as a very strong component the Swan band of the carbon molecule, C_2. The distinct maximum at 4,737 is the beginning of the vibrational band of this molecule. The presence of C_2 is confirmed by other considerably weaker groups of Swan bands, with maxima at 5,165 and 5,636A. The existence of the C_2 molecule in the effusing gases can therefore be considered as established. [See letter at end of article].

In the region from the hydrogen-delta (H δ) line to the H line of ionized calcium, there is a system of faint bands belonging to the linear molecule C_3, which is observed in the spectrum of comet heads just as the Swan bands are.

The Alphonsus spectrum differs from comet spectra, however, in the complete absence of the ultraviolet band of the CN molecule at 3,883A. Comparatively bright bands exist in the spectrum from 4,200 to 4,600A and in other regions there are large numbers of faint bands. We have not yet succeeded in determining the molecules responsible for these bands. Furthermore, all the bands have a washed-out appearance. The Swan bands should be entirely sharp on the long-wave side, but they appear indistinct for about 5 to 10A for some unknown reason.

It is possible that the observations just described will be unique for some time to come. But the existence today of internal energy and the possibility of orogenic processes (mountain formation) on the moon seem to have been established. The coincidence of the observed phenomenon with the position of the central peak can hardly have been accidental, and may indicate that the basic relief of the moon originated from within rather than from the impact of giant meteorites. The low thermal conductivity of the lunar surface layers may result from the porous character of volcanic material rather than from a dust layer.

Letter received from Dr. Kozyrev, June 6, 1960.

Dear Dr. Richardson:

I shall be very pleased if you should use my *Sky and Telescope* paper in your book. I ask you to take into consideration the following corrections based on the results of a solid study of the spectrum.

In my paper it has been erroneously stated that in the first spectrogram of Alphonsus (3 Nov. 1958, 1ʰ U.T.), the central peak is weakened in the violet rays as compared with its usual appearance and that this phenomenon may be explained by an ejection of dust. But, as a matter of fact, the central peak had the usual distribution of energy in the spectrum.

Measurements have confirmed the identification of the band 4,737A with the Swan band of the C_2 molecule. However, the band 5,165 (Swan C_2) in the spectrum of the central peak is not firmly established. The band 5,636, on the other hand, may be present in the spectrum. In any case, there is here an undoubted *increase* in brightness. The identification of the weak bands between H Delta and H with the C_3 bands cannot be considered as certain, but is rather probable.

The total amount of gas issued from the central peak should be considered as of the order of 10^6 cubic meters, if it is reduced to conditions at the earth's surface.

I am asking you to take into consideration these data.

Yours sincerely,
N. Kozyrev

* The Other Side of the Moon
—in Theory

This article, when published in 1953, constituted our best guess at the appearance of the far side of the moon. It must have taken considerable courage on Mr. Wilkins's part to go out on a limb as he did by publishing a map [Plate XIa] of the hidden side, although at the time the prospect that anyone would be able to check on it seemed remote indeed. For in 1953 who would have been rash enough to predict that only six years later we would have had a look at the far side? Very few we suspect. Yet that is exactly what happened. On October 7, 1959, Lunik III circled around the moon, took photographs of the far side, and televised them to earth. It is true that the pictures were cruder in quality than the first daguerreotype of the moon taken in 1840. Crude as they were, however, they did give us some idea of surface conditions on the hidden side of our satellite. It was no longer purely a matter of speculation and conjecture.

A very assiduous student of the moon, Wilkins has made a specialty of observing the markings on the hidden side that are occasionally brought into view by the so-called lunar librations. For it is wrong to say that the *same* side of the moon is *always* turned toward the earth. The statement requires qualification. There are two circumstances that enable us to see slightly more than half of the moon's surface at one time or another. The axis of the moon is tilted by a few degrees relative to its orbit around the earth. The result is that we alternately see a little over and under the north and south poles of the moon [Plates I, XIb]. Secondly, while the moon rotates on its axis at a uniform rate, its rate of revolution around the earth is nonuniform. Thus the revolution of the moon gets out of step with its rotation, and as a consequence a portion of the eastern or western edge is brought into view that is ordinarily hidden. This apparent swaying of the moon relative to the earth is called libration after the word *libra,* meaning a "balance," since the moon seems to tilt back and forth like the arm of a balance. Owing to the librations of the moon, in the course of time we are able to see 59 per cent of the lunar surface, leaving 41 per cent that we never see. The view we get of the far side is not very satisfactory, for the markings revealed are at the edge of the disk and hence badly distorted due to foreshortening.

Craters on the other side may reveal themselves without our actually being able to see them. We know that many craters on the visible side have long bright streaks radiating from them called rays. Wilkins detected several rays coming around the edge of the disk which led him to infer the existence of several good-sized craters on the far side. He postulated that there would be at least one with an extensive ray system comparable to that of Tycho. On rather flimsy evidence he also postulated the presence of a large dark sea on the far side.

The Soviet photographs of the far side of the moon [Plate XIb] bear scant resemblance to Wilkins's map. The far side is a surprise in that no large seas are present such as we see on the visible side. In fact, if conditions were reversed and the other side of the moon turned toward the earth, we would have quite a different conception of the nature of the lunar surface. No crater with an extensive ray system can be discerned on the photographs although the contrast between the rays and the general surface background may be too low to register. Some of the small spots on the far side may be large craters with smooth floors like that of Plato that darken toward full moon.

Despite the fact that Wilkins's map apparently fell wide of the mark, nevertheless it is of interest in representing an attempt to say something on an exceedingly difficult subject. In the accompanying article, Wilkins tells what was known about the far side of the moon in pre-Lunik days, and how he arrived at his conclusions concerning conditions there.

The Other Side of the Moon

H. PERCY WILKINS

FROM time immemorial it has been known that the moon always turns the same face toward us. Everybody knows that, unlike the sun, the face of the moon is spotted and shaded. These spots are best seen at full moon when the general appearance is that of a somewhat rough-looking human face staring at us, very much after the way in which the sphinx stares fixedly at the same spot over the sands of Egypt. The earliest savage races noticed this, and the Roman historian Plutarch wrote about "The Face in the Moon." Hence arose the age-old expression "the Man in the Moon." In one respect the faces of the moon and

H. Percy Wilkins, from *Journal of the British Interplanetary Society,* Vol. 12, No. 1, January, 1953.

the sphinx differ—"the Man in the Moon" has been staring for a much longer time. In all probability the moon man has stared at us for millions of years, long before there was any life on the earth, certainly any human life, and must have seen many strange things happen on our planet. The important thing to note is that whether the moon is a crescent, a half-moon, or full, the face still looks at us from the sky. This can mean only one thing—the moon always keeps the same side toward the earth, the other side being forever turned away from us.

Does this mean then that we know absolutely nothing about the other side and can know nothing until the first spaceships take off and men actually land on the moon? Until recently, people thought so, and all manner of curious speculations were made about the farther side. The side we see has neither air nor water, being, in fact, an arid desert, plastered over with mountains and vast ringlike objects, the so-called craters; but at one time it was seriously thought that the other side was quite different. There, we were told, were both air and water and, possibly, vegetation, animals, or even people. The idea behind this strange fancy was that the moon was oval or egg-shaped, the pointed end being directed toward us. It was argued that the face we see was a sort of gigantic mountain top sticking up out of the atmosphere and water, which were supposed to be confined to the relatively low-lying other side. This fantastic theory has long been given up and it is now known that there is neither air nor water on any part of the moon.

Although we said the moon always turned the same face toward us, the truth is that, like a drunkard, "the Man in the Moon" does sway a little from side to side and also nods up and down and this allows us to peep a little around the edge to see a part of the other side. The proper name for this swaying is "libration" and because of it we can see, at one time or another, one tenth of the other side, or over 100 miles around the edge. Apart from these peeps, why does the moon always keep the same face turned toward us? There must be some reason for this strange state of things, and it is evidently in some way due to the earth. Some power or force must have been in action to compel the moon to turn the same face toward us, and then keep it so.

This question leads us into rather deep waters, in fact to the query as to where the moon itself came from. The argument goes like this. If, as some people have thought, the moon was originally a little planet moving in a path of its own around the sun, which path at one point lay close to the earth's orbit, and eventually came so close that our own planet captured it, then there would be no reason why the moon should always turn the same face toward us, provided the moon was already solid. If, however, the moon, ages ago, was not solid but fluid, or at least plastic, or if at that time there were seas on the moon, then the attraction of the earth would raise enormous tides in the seas, which would act as most efficient brakes and eventually so slow down the moon's rotation as to cause her to always turn the same face toward us. Even with ourselves, the much weaker tides which the moon raises in our oceans are slowly, almost imperceptibly, slowing down the earth's rotation, but it will take millions of years before the earth turns one and the same face toward the moon.

On the side of the moon which faces us, the action of the once active tides must have resulted in a sort of bulge toward us, a kind of frozen tidal wave, which is, so to speak, the lever by means of which the earth, having once brought the moon to a relative fixity, keeps it so. Some people, indeed, regard the craters not as extinct volcanoes or caused by meteors striking the surface, but as due to plastic or molten matter in the interior which has been literally sucked out through weak spots, or "pinholes" in the crust, by the once gigantic tidal action of the earth.

As we have said, owing to libration, we can actually see a strip or zone, about 100 miles west of the mysterious other side all around the borders. In addition to what can actually be seen, we can trace certain light rays which are obviously converging toward foci on the remote hemisphere. Since, on the visible side, the light rays radiate from craters 20 to 50 miles in diameter, there can be little doubt that the visible foci are also craters, the approximate positions of which we can plot. Judging by analogy on both the earth and Mars, there is a sort of balancing on planetary globes, an excess of matter, i.e., a continent or extensive mountainous region, being compensated at the point diametrically opposite by a depression. On the earth we have the great continental mass of Europe and Asia, with, on the opposite side, the Pacific Ocean.

If this also holds on the moon, we might expect that the southern portion of the other side, would be largely mountainous and thus opposed to the so-called "seas" which occupy so much of the northern portion of the side which faces us. For similar reasons, the northern part would contain several "seas" or plains, but these are probably less extensive than the plains on our side, since the results of past tidal action must be far less marked there.

Taking everything into consideration, fact and surmise, what, in all probability, does the other side look like and how does it differ, both in broad outline and detail, from the side we know so well? In short, can we prepare an advance guide for the space explorers of the, probably, not far distant future?

We can conveniently divide the moon's surface into three parts. First, the portion we always see, about two fifths of the whole, then the portion we never see, also two fifths, while the remaining one fifth is a part all around the edge, half on this side and half on the other, which the swaying first brings into view and then takes out again.

Our chart [Plate XIa], the first of its kind ever published, shows the probable appearance of the moon's other side as it would be seen by anybody viewing it from a distance above the center; in other words, from a point directly away from the earth. Our planet would, indeed, be directly behind the moon and completely hidden by it when the rocket carrying the observer came within 60,000 miles. The writer has found the following features on the other side.

A large plain or "sea," probably even larger than the Mare Imbrium, or the Sea of Rains on our side, covers much of the northern part and probably extends westward with a bay on the northwest. This bay can just be detected under the most favorable conditions and has been called the Mare Incognito, or the "unknown sea," on a special section of the writer's large map of the moon.* There are also smaller plains, the general appearance being that shown on our chart. Anyone can see that if the shading was reversed, the light parts being darkened and the dark areas made light, it would roughly correspond with the distribution of light and dark areas on our side. In other words, elevations on our side correspond to depressions on the other.

As for details, craters and mountains on the light and dark areas, little can be said and nothing is known with certainty. However, we have traced light rays on our side which obviously converge to foci on the other. Since on our side light rays diverge from conspicuous craters, i.e., Tycho, Copernicus, and Kepler, there can be little doubt that there are similar craters on the other side. The converging rays show that there are three such ray centers on the northwestern part, four smaller on the eastern part near the equator and south of it. The chief ray center, probably a crater 50 or 60 miles in diameter, lies on the south about one third of the way from the center to the south limb and a little east of the central meridian. This crater is in the middle of the mountainous region, but those on the north are probably situated on the great northern plains.

Coming near the edge, or limb, we are on more secure ground. We can see the details in these regions as they are carried into view in extreme libration. Great craters, some already named, and lofty mountain ranges, lie on the southern portion. Along the top or south edge are great rings, giant craters, and between them great mountain masses towering up into the sky. Some of them can be seen in profile on the very edge itself; the highest is so lofty that it would be necessary to pile two mountains like Snowdon on top of our Mount Everest before we could equal it. It is a veritable celestial skyscraper and can occasionally be seen from the earth. As the east point is approached they become more crowded, while on the edge itself is a small plain, the Mare Orientalis. An almost continuous array of mountains runs from the southwest to the east point; they are the D'Alembert and the Doerfel mountains, some of the peaks of which rise 20,000 feet. Large craters, rivaling the finest on our side, occur along the western edge, but the north polar regions have few lofty mountains. The chief features are large, comparatively low-walled enclosures. The actual pole itself

* Editor's note: See under Wilkins, in "Suggestions for Further Reading."

lies within one of them, in striking contrast with the deep craters and lofty mountains on the south polar regions.

The more delicate features such as pits, craterlets, and clefts, which exist in great numbers on the side facing the earth, doubtless also exist on the other side, but it is quite impossible to confirm this supposition by direct observation, owing to the great foreshortening.

This sketch of the moon's other side, although of necessity imperfect and incomplete, does indicate that the same characteristic features, although with differences of detail, are found on the entire lunar globe.

Anybody on the moon in what is to us the center of its face, would naturally see the earth overhead. But as they move toward what we consider the edge, the earth would seem to get lower and lower in the sky, until, if they camped at a certain spot, the earth, although most of the time well up, would touch the horizon once every month. As a person went farther, more and more of the earth would be hidden at times until, when they reached the edge of the other side, the earth would be hidden most of the time, and would to a greater or less degree, pop into view once a month. Finally, about 130 miles from the border, the earth would just touch the horizon without any part of it becoming visible. The travelers would then be literally in an unknown world; but it is hoped that when the first spaceships take off and men actually land on the other side of the moon, they will find our chart and descriptions more or less reliable guides.

*The Other Side of the Moon
—in Fact

Like most seemingly unattainable objectives, the nature of the far side of the moon has always had a fascination for laymen and astronomers alike, a symbol of all that is remote and mysterious. Thus as we have seen, Edgar Allan Poe in "Hans Pfaal" speaks of the "dark and hideous mysteries" of the hidden side of the moon. This is quite legitimate for fictional purposes, but of course there was never anything in fact to back it up. As Wilkins points out, the hidden side of the moon is not wholly unknown to us, but relying upon earth-based telescopes it is impossible to go much farther than he has done. To learn anything more about the moon, a radically new observing technique was necessary. The ideal, of course, would be to send a man around to the far side of the moon where he could have a look at it at first hand. Doubtless every selenographer has envisaged himself in such a situation. It was the sort of thing one dreamed about after a hard night at the telescope.

The Russian automatic interplanetary station called Lunik III was launched on October 4, 1959. This vehicle was designed especially for the purpose of obtaining photographs of the moon, in particular the far side of the moon. To carry out this program it was necessary to make the station adhere very closely to a predetermined orbit that would put it into precisely the right position relative to the moon at the right time. It is much more difficult to put a rocket into a round-the-moon trip than a hit-the-moon trip. If we don't care how hard the rocket crash-lands, it is (relatively) easy to put it into an orbit that will intercept the moon in its path. But to make a rocket curve around the moon and return to earth means that some very critical conditions must be satisfied. If it were possible to control the rocket while in flight, the problem would not be nearly so formidable. As it is, however, the whole path of the rocket is predetermined by its position and velocity at burnout. If the initial velocity is only a few hundredths of a mile per second too low it will fail to reach the moon. If a trifle too high, it will go past the moon and orbit around the sun. It is commonly supposed that the gravitational attraction of the moon will greatly influence the motion of the rocket. But since the mass of the moon is only $1/81$ the mass of the earth, it seldom has much effect on the motion of the rocket. The

84

rocket has to pass very close to the moon (within a few thousand miles) to have its path altered radically. Hence, if we want to count on the moon for help in producing a desired change in the motion of a rocket we need a guidance system that is accurate to a very high degree.

The plans for Lunik III called for photographing the moon's far side when it was in the crescent phase as seen from the earth. Most of the far side would then be illuminated so that a single photograph, if successful, would reveal most of the hidden surface. The disadvantage is that the surface is illuminated under flat lighting so that the markings are not thrown into relief by shadow. Often at full moon nothing but the outlines of the craters can be discerned if they do not disappear entirely. Only the bright and dark areas on the surface stand out strongly.

The station was supposed to photograph the moon when in a straight line with the sun and moon at a distance of from 37,500 to 43,500 miles from the lunar surface, with the earth slightly to one side of the line between the sun and moon. A light-sensitive orientation device actuated by the sun kept the camera trained in the opposite direction on the moon. Accurate focusing was insured by means of a signal received from an optical device attached to the camera, thus permitting automatic photographing.

To be successful, the station had to be put into a path that would allow it to yield the maximum amount of information during the first loop of its flight when at a short distance from the earth. This meant securing the best possible conditions for radio communication with the station from points within the Soviet Union.

Flight around the moon followed by return to earth can in theory be achieved in many ways. From a practicable standpoint, however, some of these paths are much more desirable than others. A rocket launched from the Northern Hemisphere that passes the moon at a great distance will return to earth from the side of the Southern Hemisphere. This makes it difficult for stations in the Northern Hemisphere to receive information from the rocket. Such a drawback is avoided if the rocket is forced to move in a path that takes it south of the moon by only a few thousand miles. At this close distance, the attraction of the moon for the rocket causes it to deviate toward the north. The result is that the rocket returns to earth from the side of the Northern Hemisphere, where it is easily kept under observation. Although the station upon its first return escapes destruction in the earth's atmosphere by a wide margin, nevertheless its lifetime is limited. Due to the disturbing influence of the sun, its distance from the earth at each approach is steadily decreasing. Eventually it will plunge into the atmosphere and burn up.

The photographs of the moon so obtained, crude as they are, do however give us some idea of conditions on the moon's far side. Probably the most valuable information obtained from Lunik III is that, contrary to expectations, the far side of the moon does not resemble the near side. The large dark areas called maria, which make up the familiar face of the man in the moon, are almost entirely absent. Why there should be maria on one side of the moon and not on the other will give selenographers something new to argue about. As we have seen in the articles by Gold and Baldwin the nature of the maria is still uncertain.

From the Soviet photograph, it appears that if the far side of the moon were turned in our direction we would have formed an entirely different conception of conditions on the lunar surface. On our side, the maria dominate the surface. On the far side, they are of minor importance. The Soviet photos also show no crater like Tycho with a bright ray system such as Wilkins postulated. And of course the large sea which he envisaged is also apparently absent. This shows how far wrong we may be when guessing at the nature of the nearest of the heavenly bodies, even when half revealed to us.

It is worth noting in passing that the Russians were not only the first to photograph the back side of the moon, but they were also the first to land an object on the surface of the moon. According to Soviet reports contact with the moon was made on Sunday, September 13, 1959, at 21^h 02^m Greenwich Time, or 4:02 P.M., Eastern Standard Time. Actual contact with the moon is said to have been witnessed by Niklos Lovas of the Csillebérc Observatory of the Hungarian Academy of Sciences. (Nothing is known about this observatory which is not among the observatories of the world listed in the *American Ephemeris and Nautical Almanac*.) The photograph [Plate XIVc] shows astronomer Lovas pointing to the spot where he saw the rocket strike in the Palus Putredinis [putrid swamp, Plate XX], at approximately 2° west longitude, 27° north latitude. He said he observed a giant cloud of dust that was raised when the rocket hit. This must be rated as an exceedingly lucky observation since the path of the rocket could hardly have been known accurately enough to predict the landing place. Also, owing to the absence of atmosphere, the dust would have settled rapidly, probably only being visible for a few minutes at most. The moon on September 13, 1959, was at the gibbous phase midway between first quarter and full, and *not* at the phase shown in the illustration which is near last quarter. The Russians are said to have placed the USSR emblem of the hammer and sickle on the moon's surface, but they denied any territorial claim.

*

The Other Side of the Moon

IN EVOLVING the complex means for taking photographs and transmitting the pictures of the hidden side of the moon from the automatic interplanetary station, the task was successfully accomplished of creating a phototelevision system to obtain a high-quality half-tone image and transmit it over distances measured in hundreds of thousands of kilometers.

In doing this a number of complicated scientific and engineering problems have been solved.

While the photographs were being taken, the orientation system kept the station in a position whereby the moon's disc was directly in front of the camera lenses.

The construction of the phototelevision apparatus insured that it would be able to operate under the difficult conditions of space flight; in the conditions of the harmful action of cosmic radiation, the photographic supplies were preserved intact and the apparatus for processing the photographic materials and other equipment worked normally in conditions of weightlessness.

In transmitting pictures over a large distance, using a very low-capacity radio transmitter, the speed at which pictures were transmitted was several thousand times lower than is the case with ordinary television stations.

In taking these first photographs of the reverse side of the moon, it was desirable to photograph as large a part as possible of its unknown surface. This led to the necessity of photographing the fully illuminated disc, the contrast of which is always far less than when there is illumination from the side which creates shadows from the details of relief.

To insure high-quality transmission of low-contrast pictures, the television apparatus was provided with automatic adjustment of the scanner tube's brightness. Self-adjusting devices were applied also to insure reliable and faultless operation of the setup in changing regimes.* The co-ordination and guidance of the work of all units, including the electronic arrangements and the optical, mechanical, and photochemical installations, were effected through a special system of automatics and programming.

* Editor's note: The meaning of "changing regimes" here is not entirely clear. It may refer to switching lenses on the camera from a focal length of 200 to 500 mm.

From *Soviet News*, October, 1959.

The phototelevision apparatus of the interplanetary station has the following basic structure. A camera with two lenses having focal lengths of 200 and 500 mm. with the help of which pictures were taken simultaneously in two different scales. The lens, with a focal length of 200 mm., produced an image of the disc which fitted completely into the frame. The large-scale image produced by the lens with a 500 mm. focal length was bigger than the frame, and gave a more detailed picture of this side of the moon's disc.

The photographs were made with automatic changes of exposure to obtain negatives with the most advantageous densities. The photographing lasted about 40 minutes, during which time the hidden side of the moon was photographed repeatedly.

The photographing began at a command signal given after the lenses had been focused on the moon. The subsequent process of photographing and processing the film was done entirely automatically according to a set program. Special 35 mm. film was used which can be processed at high temperatures.

In order to prevent the film from being fogged due to the action of cosmic radiation, a special protection was provided, chosen on the basis of investigations conducted with the help of the Soviet Sputniks and space rockets.

After it had been exposed, the film entered a small automatic developing and fixing device.

In treating it, a special process was used which minimized the dependence of the parameters of the negative on temperature. The necessary measures were taken to prevent this process from being upset by conditions of weightlessness. After the film had been treated, it was dried and the moisture was absorbed, thus insuring its preservation. Then the film passed into a special case and was prepared for the transmission of the picture.

Reference marks had been made on the film in advance, part of which were developed on the earth, and the rest on the station while the shots of the far side of the moon were being treated. These marks, or signs, when transmitted to the earth, made it possible to control the processes of photographic treatment and the transmission of the pictures.

To transform the image on the negative, a small scanning tube with a high resolving capacity and a stable photoelectronic multiplier were used.

Transmission of the pictures to the earth was done in the same way as films are transmitted by television stations.

In order to deflect the ray of the electronic-ray tube, economic low-frequency scanning devices were used. Magnification and setting of the signals of the pictures were effected by a special narrow-band stabilized amplifier which automatically compensated the influence of changes in the average density of the negative on the outgoing signal. All the schemes were carried out in the main with transistors.

Provision was made for the pictures to be transmitted to two regimes: slow transmission over large distances and fast transmission for shorter distances as the station approached the earth. The television system made it possible, in accordance with the conditions of transmission, to change the number of lines into which the picture was broken up. The maximum number of lines reached 1,000 per shot.

To synchronize the transmitting and receiving scanning devices, a method was used which insured high resistance to interference and steady operation of the apparatus.

The pictures of the moon were transmitted from the automatic interplanetary station along the radio communication lines serving at the time for measurements of the parameters of the movement of the station itself; that is to say, distance, velocity, and angle co-ordinates, and also for the telemetric transmission of the results of the scientific experiments. The various devices on the station were switched on and off and their regimes were changed by special orders transmitted from the earth over the same radio line.

The pictures of the moon were transmitted and all the other operations on the line of radio communication with the station were carried out by means of continuous radiations of radio waves, as distinct from the impulse radiation used previously in certain cases. This is the first time such a combination of functions in a single radio communication line, working under permanent radiation, has been attempted. It insured reliable radio communication even at maximum distances, with the least possible expenditure of energy on the station itself.

Radio communication with the station consisted of two parts: one line "Earth–Station," and another line "Station–Earth," and included command devices, powerful radio transmitters, supersensitive receiving and recording devices, systems stationed at radio communication points on the earth, and also transmitting, receiving, and antenna devices on the interplanetary station. In addition, command and programming radiotechnical installations were set up on the station.

The entire apparatus of radio communication lines both on the station and on the earth was duplicated in order to increase the reliability of communication. In the event of one of the radio-engineering instruments on board going out of commission, or the resources needed for its work being exhausted, it could be replaced by the reserve instrument through a corresponding order being given from a guidance point on the earth.

The pictures of the moon were transmitted on command from the earth. At those times, the television apparatus on board was switched on, the photo film was moved, and the television apparatus was switched on to the transmitters. As a result, the law of changes in brightness, along the lines into which the image was broken up, was transmitted to the earth.

The total volume of scientific information transmitted by radio, including the photographs of the moon, far exceeds the volume of information that was transmitted from the first and second Soviet space rockets.

To secure the reliable transmission of this information under conditions of a high level of cosmic radiation, an especially effective method of radio communication was used guaranteeing the minimum expenditure of energy by the power-feeding sources on board.

Because of the need to economize in electric power, the power of the radio transmitters on the station was established at a few watts. Semiconductors and other modern parts and materials were used in the receiving and transmitting radio apparatus on board. Particular attention was paid to making the instruments as small and as light as possible.

An idea of the difficulties encountered in insuring reliable radio communication with the station can be obtained by estimating what part of the power emitted by the radio transmitter on board actually comes down to the receiving devices on the earth.

To insure that communication with the station is not suspended as it rotates, the station's aerial emits radio signals evenly in all directions so that the power of emission for a unit of surface will be the same for all the points of the imaginary sphere in which the station is centered.

The part of the power transmitted to the earth receiving aerial is determined by the ratio of the effective area as of the receiving aerial to the surface of the sphere with a radius equal to the distance from the station to the receiving point. For that reason, large receiving aerials are used to intercept the signals from the station.

However, even in this case, when the station is at a maximum distance from the earth, the part of the power emitted by the transmitter on board that is actually intercepted is 100 million times smaller than the average power intercepted by an ordinary television set. Extremely sensitive receiving devices with low static must be used to pick up such weak signals.

The static produced by the earth receiving devices consists of the static cosmic radiation picked up by the aerial and the static produced by the receiver itself, which is reduced to a minimum by a number of special measures. As a rule, the reduction of the static is connected with a reduction of the speed at which information is transmitted.

In view of what has been said, methods of processing and transmitting signals were used in the radio communication line on the station and on the earth's receiving points that reduce the static level to the maximum degree and retain the permissible speed of transmission.

The signals transmitting photographs of the moon were recorded by special television devices on a photographic film; by magnetic recording apparatus with high stability of the magnetic tape speed; by skytron (electronic-ray tubes which keep the image on the screen for a considerable time) ; and by open recording instruments taking down the image on electrochemical paper. The results obtained by all these recording methods are being used in studying the hidden side of the moon.

The television system on the automatic interplanetary station has transmitted pictures over a distance of up to 470,000 km. [292,000 miles]; thereby the possibility of transmitting half-tone pictures of a high degree of accuracy, without any essential specific distortions in the process of radio wave propagation, has for the first time been confirmed experimentally.

The Moon's Hidden Face. The moon was photographed from the interplanetary space station at the moment when the station was on the line connecting the sun and the moon, that is to say, when the moon was an almost completely illuminated disc with respect to the station.

The photographs have recorded a part of the moon's surface invisible from the earth and a small area with already known formations. This latter area on the photographs has made it possible to connect the previously unseen features of the lunar surface with those already known, and thus determine their selenographical co-ordinates.

The moon's features visible from the earth photographed by the interplanetary station include: the Humboldt Sea, the Sea of Crises, the Marginal Sea, the Smith Sea, a part of the Southern Sea, and others.

These seas, located at the very edge of the moon and visible from the earth, owing to perspective distortion appear to us to be narrow and long, and their real shape has hitherto been indefinite. On the photographs taken from the interplanetary station, these seas are situated far from the visible edge of the moon and their shape is distorted only to an insignificant extent by perspective. Thus, we have for the first time learned the real shape of a number of lunar formations.

It is noticeable that mountainous areas predominate on the invisible part of the lunar surface, while there are very few seas like those in the visible part. Crater seas in the southern and near-equatorial regions stand out sharply.

Of the seas situated near the edge of the visible part and greatly foreshortened, the photographs clearly show, almost without distortion, the Humboldt Sea, the Marginal Sea, the Smith Sea, and the Southern Sea. It appears that a large part of the Southern Sea lies on the reverse of the moon, and its "coastline" has a tortuous configuration.

The Smith Sea is rounder than the Southern Sea, and on its southern side a mountainous region cuts deep into it. The Marginal Sea is somewhat elongated in a "northerly" direction and has a depression in the opposite direction from the Sea of Crises.

The Humboldt Sea has a peculiar pearlike shape. The entire area adjoining the western edge of the moon's far side (i.e., the Marginal Sea) has a reflecting power intermediate between the mountain regions and the seas. As regards its reflecting power, it resembles the region of the moon lying between the Tycho and Petavius craters and the Sea of Nectar.

South-southeast of the Humboldt Sea, on the border of the aforementioned region, there runs a mountain range 2,000 km. [1,240 miles] long, crossing the equator and extending to the southern hemisphere. Beyond the mountain range is an extensive continent with a heightened reflecting capacity.

A crater sea some 300 km. [186 miles] in diameter lies in the region between latitudes 20° and 30° N. and longitudes 140° and 160° W. In its southern part, this sea ends in a bay. There is a large crater more than 100 km. [62 miles] in diameter with a dark bed and a bright central hill surrounded by a broad, light bank, in the southern hemisphere, in the area of latitude 30° and longitude plus 130°.

To the east of this range, in the area of latitude 30° N. is a group of four medium-sized craters; the biggest has a diameter of some 70 km. [43 miles]. A separate round crater is to be seen southwest of this group in the area of latitude of 10° N. and longitude plus 110°. On the western edge of the southern hemisphere there are two regions with considerably lower reflecting power.

Besides that, the photographs show regions with somewhat higher or lower reflecting power and numerous small details. It will be possible to establish the nature of these details and their shape and dimensions after a thorough study of all the photographs.

The televising, for the first time, of pictures of the hidden part of the moon by the interplanetary station opens up wide prospects for studying the planets of our solar system.

THE TRIP TO THE

MOON

*

* *The Journey to the Moon*

Posterity may find us lacking in many respects, but surely it can never accuse us of being backward when it comes to the conquest of space. The flight to the moon has been anticipated so long that when it happens it is likely to come as something of an anticlimax. We have gone to the moon so often in imagination that we are beginning to regard it as an accomplished fact. In our own minds it is already done.

It is doubtful if there is anyone in the world better qualified to talk on the practical aspects of the moon trip than Dr. Wernher von Braun. He has been interested in rocketry since early youth. He was one of the top men who worked on the V-2 at Peenemünde. After the war, he came to the United States to work on rockets for us. His primary interest in rocketry has always been in space travel rather than in the development of the rocket as a military weapon. In fact, during the war he was imprisoned for a couple of weeks by the Nazis on this very charge. Since coming to this country, he has been in the forefront of those who feel confident that we can ultimately send men to the moon and planets. He is, of course, an engineer and not an astronomer. A knowledge of astronomy, however, is only of incidental importance in this field. Indeed the exploration of the moon and planets really will not belong to astronomy at all but will lie more in the realm of geophysics.

Dr. von Braun has always had large ideas on the subject of space travel which he has not hesitated to state with confidence, and nowhere is this better shown than in this account of an expedition to the moon. He speaks of it as a "pioneer" expedition. Evidently it is not intended to be a description of the "first" expedition to the moon. We will feel immensely proud of ourselves when we put the first man on the moon and get him safely back to earth again. A fifty-man expedition to the moon in three rocket ships such as von Braun describes here will not come until much later.

One has the uneasy feeling that many of the operations described here will not turn out to be nearly as simple as they are made to sound. Assembling a ship in space will be an enormously complex operation. The various parts should arrive in space with precisely the same velocities. But this will be next to impossible. If the components of a ship differ in velocity by only a few hundredths of a mile per second they will quickly drift apart. One can picture workmen propelling themselves frantically about with hand-operated reaction

95

jets trying desperately to keep track of their material, like cowboys trying to round up an unruly herd of cattle.

Assuming the ships can be assembled in space, the trip to the moon itself should be a relatively easy matter. There will be no storms or cross traffic on the way. Meteorites would constitute the only hazard but it seems these would not be too serious a menace. The next major operation will come when we try to set the ship down on the moon. We have to make the velocity of the ship precisely match that of the lunar surface. It will take some delicate maneuvering to set the ship down without a bump, but von Braun evidently feels confident it can be done successfully. After effecting a landing, we have to do some intensive exploratory work and then return to earth. Doubtless there will be many heartbreaking discouragements before we read of a trip to the moon that goes off as smoothly as the one described here.

*

Man on the Moon — The Journey

WERNHER VON BRAUN

HERE is how we shall go to the moon. The pioneer expedition, fifty scientists and technicians, will take off from the space station's orbit in three clumsy-looking but highly efficient rocket ships. They won't be streamlined: all travel will be in space, where there is no air to impede motion. Two will be loaded with propellant for the five-day, 239,000-mile trip and the return journey. The third, which will not return, will carry only enough propellant for a one-way trip; the extra room will be filled with supplies and equipment for the scientists' six-week stay.

On the outward voyage, the rocket ships will hit a top speed of 19,500 miles per hour about thirty-three minutes after departure. Then the motors will be stopped, and the ships will fall the rest of the way to the moon.

Such a trip takes a great deal of planning. For a beginning, we must decide what flight path to follow, how to construct the ships, and where to land. But the project could be completed within the next twenty-five years. There are no problems involved to which we don't have the answers—or the ability to find them—right now.

Wernher von Braun, from *Collier's,* October 18, 1952.

I. Libration in longitude as shown by two photographs of the full moon. Compare, for instance, the distance from Aristarchus to the edge of the disc in both cases.

II. The moon, age 14 days. Notice the dominant rays spreading from Tycho, and the shorter ray systems from craters such as Copernicus, Kepler, and Aristarchus.

IIIa. The moon, age 22 days. The terminator is the boundary between light and shadow. The craters that lie along the terminator are thrown into sharp relief by the low sun.

IIIb. The moon, age 24.3 days. The ray systems about Kepler and Aristarchus begin to fade as the sun sinks further toward the horizon.

MOUNT WILSON AND PALOMAR OBSERVATORI

IV. Mare Imbrium as it appears today. Lava flows have buried the moon's greatest crater and now cover
an area of 400,000 square miles. (In this and the facing illustration, north is to the top.)

V. A suggestion as to how Mare Imbrium was formed over four billion years ago by a meteorite crashing through the moon's northeast face. See text by Ralph Baldwin.

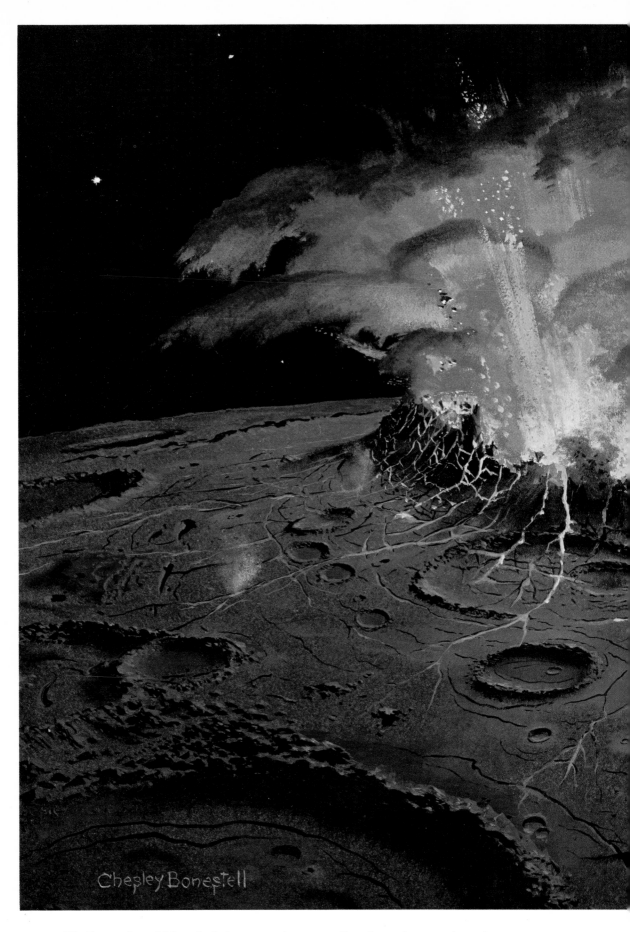

VI. Formation of Mare Imbrium, seen from 50 miles above the moon's surface.

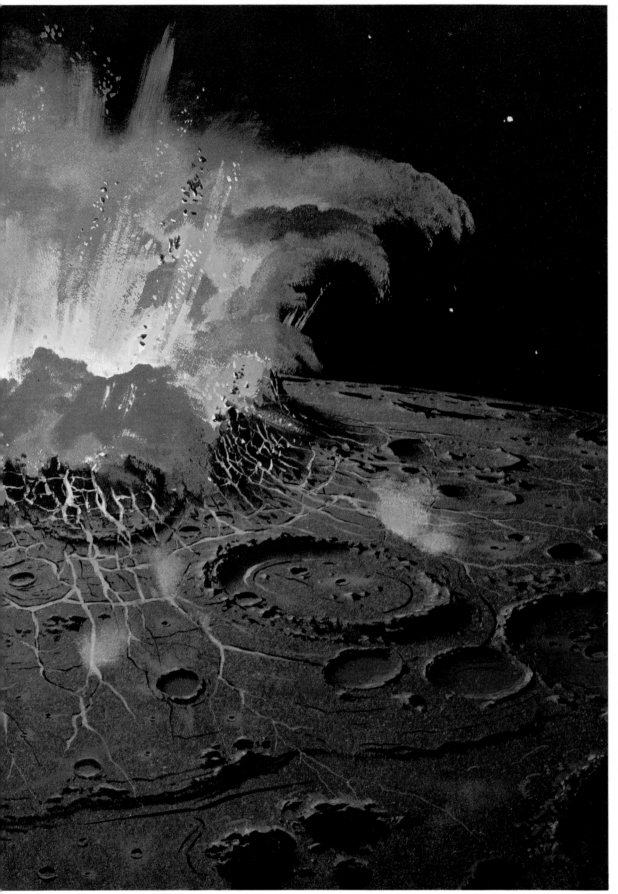

PAINTING BY CHESLEY BONESTELL

VII. Southern portion of the moon, age 24 days. Gassendi, on the northern *(bottom)* border of the Mare Humorum, measures 55 miles across.

VIII. Sinus Iridum and the Jura Mountains (pictured on the jacket of this book). Harpalus, the separate crater to the north *(bottom)* in Sinus Roris, has already been used by Hollywood as a lunar landing site.

IX. Mare Serenitatis *(bottom)* and part of Mare Tranquillitatis. Pressure ridges and rills are clearly visible in the lava.

MOUNT WILSON AND PALOMAR OBSERVATORIES

X. Photograph of Clavius with the 200-inch telescope. The crater is 145 miles across and its walls rise to 16,000 feet above the interior plain.

XIa. The far side of the moon, as suggested by t English astronomer H. P. Wilkins in 1953: fro the Journal of the British Interplanetary Socie Mare Crisium and Mare Foecunditatis can seen on the western limb. (In this map, north to the top.)

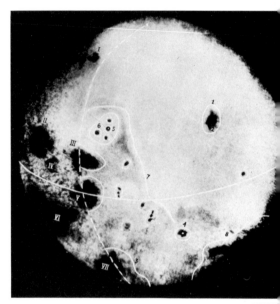

XIb. The far side of the moon, as photographed from the Russian Lunik III in 1959. The continuous line represents the lunar equator. The broken line indicates the border between the hemispheres visible and invisible from earth. (North is to the top.)

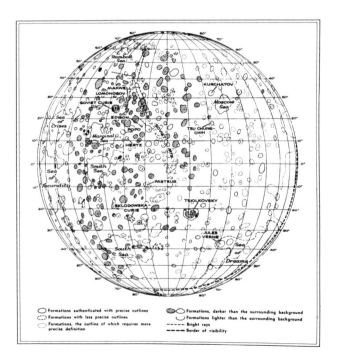

XIc. Map of the far side of the moon. Compa the features as labeled with the photograph abov

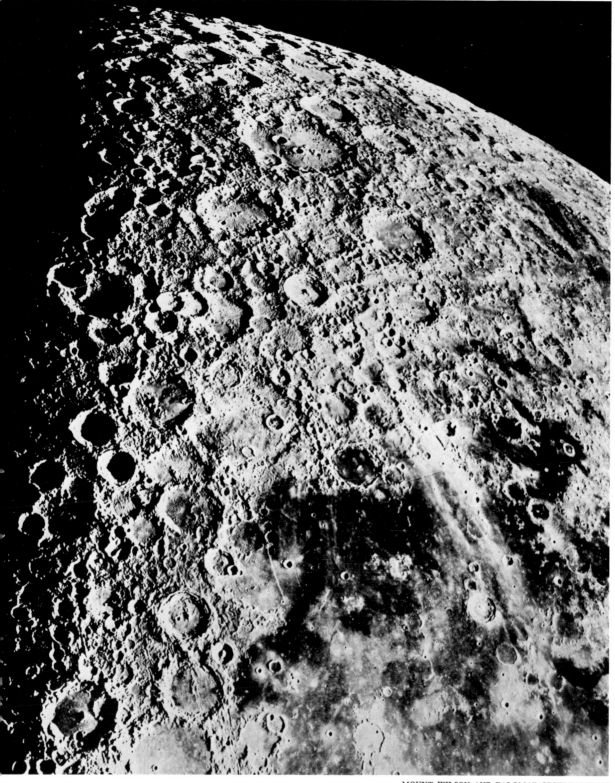

XII. Southern portion of the moon at last quarter, showing Clavius, Tycho, the Straight Wall, and Arzachel, Alphonsus, and Ptolemaeus.

XIIIa. From left to right, the craters Ptolemaeus, Alphonsus, Alpetragius, and Arzachel. The white line, superimposed on a Lick Observatory photograph, indicates the position of the spectograph slit during N. A. Kozyrev's observation of a volcanic process on November 3, 1958.

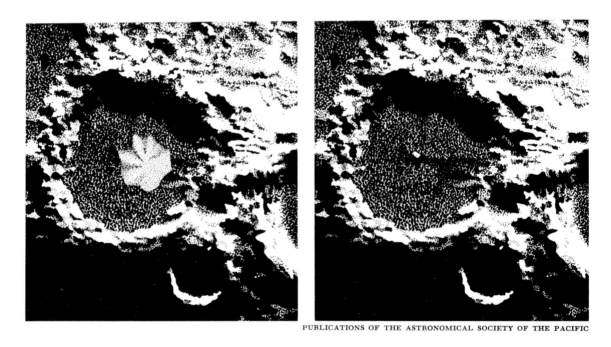

XIIIb,c. The left-hand drawing shows the crater Alphonsus as it appeared to H. F. Poppendiek and W. H. Bond on the evening of November 18, 1958. The right-hand drawing shows the crater as it appeared to them one month later. (North is to the left in all three illustrations on this page.)

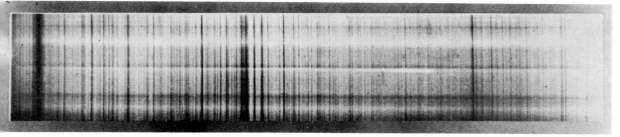

OUTER SHADOW OF WEST WALL			
SUNLIT INNER WEST WALL			
		SHADOW OF CENTRAL PEAK	
INNER SHADOW OF EAST WALL	EMISSION	SUNLIT CENTRAL PEAK	
SUNLIT OUTER EAST WALL			

934 3968   4102   4227   4340   4667   4861   5184
H K   H δ H γ H β

XIVa,b. Spectrogram made by N. A. Kozyrev of the region of Alphonsus from 3:00 to 3:30 Universal Time, November 3, 1958. The schematic diagram below indicates the presence of the strong emission originating very close to the central peak. Exposures taken before and after this spectrum show no trace of the bright emission band.

XIVc. Miklós Lovas of the Hungarian Academy of Sciences points to Palus Putredinis in Mare Imbrium where he observed a cloud of dust raised by the impact of a Soviet rocket on September 13, 1959.

XV. Eratosthenes and Copernicus viewed with the 200-inch telescope. As shown in Plate II, Copernicus
is the center of the second most important ray system on the moon. No rays are
visible under this illumination, however.

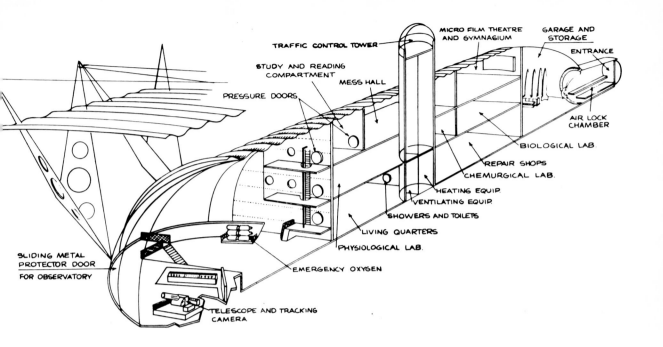

TRAFFIC CONTROL TOWER

MICRO FILM THEATRE
AND GYMNASIUM

GARAGE AND
STORAGE

STUDY AND READING
COMPARTMENT

ENTRANCE

MESS HALL

PRESSURE DOORS

AIR LOCK
CHAMBER

BIOLOGICAL LAB.

REPAIR SHOPS

CHEMURGICAL LAB.

HEATING EQUIP.

VENTILATING EQUIP.

SLIDING METAL
PROTECTOR DOOR
FOR OBSERVATORY

SHOWERS AND TOILETS

LIVING QUARTERS

PHYSIOLOGICAL LAB.

EMERGENCY OXYGEN

TELESCOPE AND TRACKING
CAMERA

JOURNAL OF THE BRITISH INTERPLANETARY SOCIETY

XVIa,b. Scale model of a moon building suggested by J. S. Rinehart. Cut-away drawing of the interior shows pressure doors between the main areas to prevent loss of internal pressure should a meteorite puncture the building wall. Entrance is made through an air lock (right). A meteoritic shield 480 by 380 feet and 83 feet above ground covers the building. The building is 65 feet high and 340 feet long.

PAINTING BY CHESLEY B

XVII. An eclipse of the sun by the earth as seen from the moon. The earth's atmosphere imparts a reddish hue to the sun's rays. Beyond the area of the eclipse *(background)* the normal blue-white light of the sun falls on the moon.

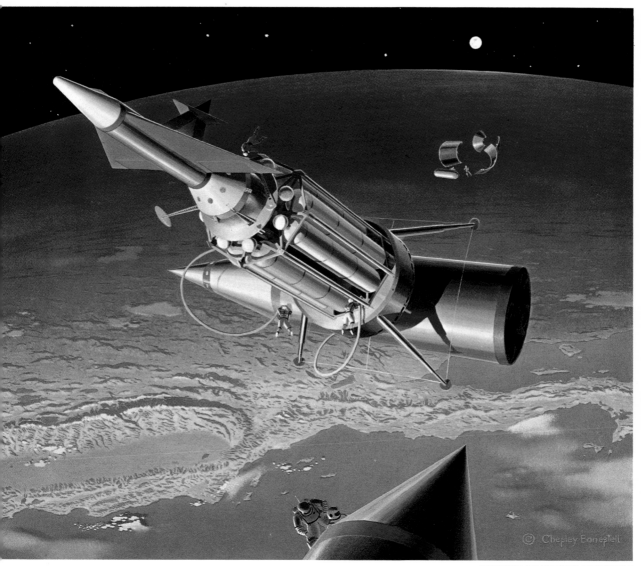

XVIII. The tanks of a moon rocket's third stage are being refilled while in orbit 1,075 miles above the coast of California. Only the winged fifth stage will return to earth after the moon journey.

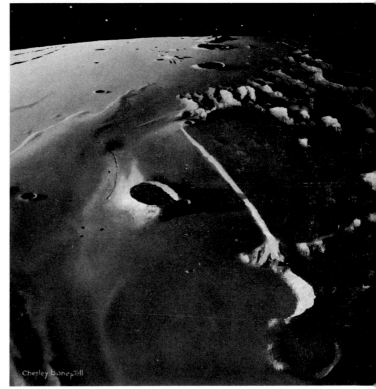

XIX. The Straight Wall seen from the north at sunset, 30 miles above the moon's surface. This great fault in Mare Nubium is 60 miles long and from 500 to 1,500 feet in height. Birt, the crater to the left, is 11 miles across.

XX. Looking south toward Aristil lus *(foreground)* and Autolycus from 50 miles above the surface. Palus Putre dinis and the Appennine Mountains can be seen in the distance. The time is sunset.

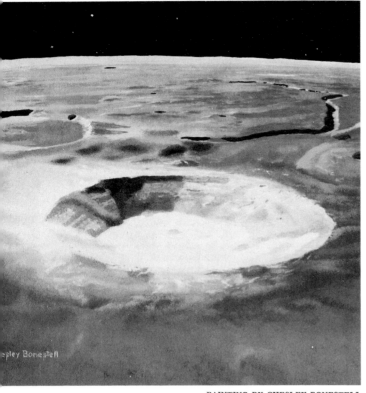

XXI. Aristarchus *(foreground)*, Herodotus *(left)*, and the Serpentine Valley seen from 30 miles above the surface, looking north with the sun almost directly overhead. When the moon is full, Aristarchus is the brightest spot on the moon and has often been mistaken for an erupting volcano.

PAINTING BY CHESLEY BONESTELL

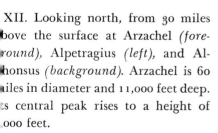

XII. Looking north, from 30 miles above the surface at Arzachel *(fore-ground)*, Alpetragius *(left)*, and Alphonsus *(background)*. Arzachel is 60 miles in diameter and 11,000 feet deep. Its central peak rises to a height of ,000 feet.

PAINTING BY CHESLEY BONESTELL

XXIII. The landing. The rocket's third stage slows its descent to the moon's surface, 500 miles below. The cargo ship in the distance will remain on the moon and carries no fuel for a return journey.

XXIV. The now empty fuel tanks are unloaded on the moon. The Milky Way shines brilliantly overhead, while in the distance the sun is about to rise.

XXV. In the earth-light reflected from the Pacific Ocean a group of spacemen explore the lunar surface
The rising sun illuminates the distant mountain tops.

First, where shall we land? We may have a wide choice, once we have had a close look at the moon. We'll get that look on a preliminary survey flight. A small rocket ship taking off from the space station will take us to within 50 miles of the moon to get pictures of its meteor-pitted surface—including the "back" part, never visible from the earth.

We'll study the photographs for a suitable site. Several considerations limit our selection. Because the moon's surface has 14,600,000 square miles—about one thirteenth that of the earth—we won't be able to explore more than a small area in detail, perhaps part of a section 500 miles in diameter. Our scientists want to see as many kinds of lunar features as possible, so we'll pick a spot of particular interest to them. We want radio contact with the earth, too; that means we'll have to stick to the moon's "face," for radio waves won't reach across space to any point the eye won't reach.

We can't land at the moon's equator because its noonday temperatures reach an unbearable 220° F., more than hot enough to boil water. We can't land where the surface is too rugged, because we need a flat place to set down. Yet the site can't be too flat, either—grain-sized meteors constantly bombard the moon at speeds of several miles a second; we'll have to set up camp in a crevice where we have protection from these bullets.

There's one section of the moon that meets all our requirements, and unless something better turns up on closer inspection, that's where we'll land. It's an area called Sinus Roris, or "Dewy Bay," on the northern branch of a plain known as Oceanus Procellarum, or "Stormy Ocean" (so called by early astronomers who thought the moon's plains were great seas). Dr. Fred L. Whipple, chairman of Harvard University's astronomy department, says Sinus Roris is ideal for our purpose—about 650 miles from the lunar north pole, where the daytime temperature averages a reasonably pleasant 40 degrees and the terrain is flat enough to land on, yet irregular enough to hide in. With a satisfactory site located, we start our detailed planning.

To save fuel and time, we want to take the shortest practical course. The moon moves around the earth in an elliptical path once every 27.3 days. The space station, our point of departure, circles the earth once every two hours. Every two weeks, their paths are such that a rocket ship from the space station will intercept the moon in just five days. The best conditions for the return trip will occur two weeks later, and again two weeks after that. With their stay limited to mulitiples of two weeks, our scientists have set themselves a six-week limit for the first exploration of the moon—long enough to accomplish some constructive research, but not long enough to require a prohibitive supply of essentials like liquid oxygen, water, and food.

Six months before our scheduled take-off, we begin piling up construction materials, supplies, and equipment at the space station. This operation is a massive, impressive one, involving huge, shuttling, cargo rocket ships, scores of hard-working handlers, and tremendous amounts of equipment. Twice a day, pairs of sleek rocket transports from the earth sweep into the satellite's orbit and swarms of workers unload the 36 tons of cargo each carries. With the arrival of the first shipment of material, work on the first of the three moon-going space craft gets under way, picking up intensity as more and more equipment arrives.

The supplies are not stacked inside the space station; they're just left floating in space. They don't have to be secured, and here's why: the satellite is traveling around the earth at 15,840 miles an hour; at that speed, it can't be affected by the earth's gravity, so it doesn't fall, and it never slows down because there's no air resistance. The same applies to any other object brought into the orbit at the same speed: to park beside the space station, a rocket ship merely adjusts its speed to 15,840 miles per hour; and it, too, becomes a satellite. Crates moved out of its hold are traveling at the same speed in relation to the earth, so they also are weightless satellites.

As the weeks pass and the unloading of cargo ships continues, the construction area covers several littered square miles. Tons of equipment lie about—aluminum girders, collapsed nylon-and-plastic fuel tanks, rocket motor units, turbopumps, bundles of thin aluminum plate, a great many nylon bags containing smaller parts. It's a bewildering scene, but not to the moon-ship builders. All construction parts are color-coded with blue-tipped cross braces fitting into blue sockets, red joining members keyed to others of the same color, and so forth. Work proceeds swiftly.

In fact, the workers accomplish wonders, considering the obstacles confronting a man forced to struggle with unwieldly objects in space. The men move clumsily, hampered by bulky pressurized suits equipped with such necessities of space life as air conditioning, oxygen tanks, walkie-talkie radios, and tiny rocket motors for propulsion. The work is laborious, for although objects are weightless they still have inertia. A man who shoves a one-ton girder makes it move all right, but he makes himself move, too. As his inertia is less than the girder's, he shoots backward much farther than he pushes the big piece of metal forward.

The small, personal rocket motors help the workers move some of the construction parts; the big stuff is hitched to space taxis, tiny pressurized rocket vehicles used for short trips outside the space station.

As the framework of the new rocket ships takes form, big, folded nylon-and-plastic bundles are pumped full of air; they become spherical, and plastic astro-domes are fitted to the top and sides of each. Other sacks are pumped full of propellant, and balloon into the shapes of globes and cylinders. Soon the three moon-going spaceships begin to emerge in their final form. The two round-trip ships resemble an arrangement of hourglasses inside a metal framework, but instead of hourglasses they have central structures which look like great silos.

For Protection Against Meteors. To guard against meteors, all vital parts of the three craft—propellant tanks, personnel spheres, cargo cabin—are given a thin covering of sheet metal, set on studs which leave at least a one-inch space between this outer shield and the inside wall. The covering, called a meteor bumper, will take the full impact of the flying particles (we don't expect to be struck by any meteors much larger than a grain of sand) and will cause them to disintegrate before they can do damage.

For protection against excessive heat, all parts of the three rocket ships are painted white, because white absorbs little of the sun's radiation. Then, to guard against cold, small black patches are scattered over the tanks and personnel spheres. The patches are covered by white blinds, automatically controlled by thermostats. When the blinds on the sunny side are open, the spots absorb heat and warm the cabins and tanks; when the blinds are closed, an all-white surface is exposed to the sun, permitting little heat to enter. When the blinds on the shaded side are open, the black spots radiate heat and the temperature drops.

Now we're ready to take off from the space station's orbit to the moon.

The bustle of our departure—hurrying space taxis, the nervous last-minute checks by engineers, the loading of late cargo, and finally the take-off itself—will be watched by millions. Television cameras on the space station will transmit the scene to receivers all over the world. And people on the earth's dark side will be able to turn from their screens to catch a fleeting glimpse of light—high in the heavens—the combined flash of ninety rocket motors, looking from the earth like the sudden birth of a new short-lived star.

Our departure is slow. The big rocket ships rise ponderously, one after the other, green flames streaming from their batteries of rockets, and then they pick up speed. Actually, we don't need to gain *much* speed. The velocity required to get us to our destination is 19,500 miles an hour, but we've had a running start; while "resting" in the space station's orbit, we were really streaking through space at 15,840 miles an hour. We need an additional 3,660 miles an hour.

Thirty-three minutes from take-off we have it. Now we cut off our motors; momentum and the moon's gravity will do the rest.

The moon itself is visible to us as we coast through space, but it's so far off to one side that it's hard to believe we won't miss it. In the five days of our journey, though, it will travel a great distance, and so will we; at the end of that time we shall reach the farthest point, or apogee, of our elliptical course, and the moon should be right in front of us.

The earth is visible, too—an enormous ball, most of it bulking pale black against the deeper black of space, but with a wide crescent of daylight where the sun strikes it. Within the crescent, the continents enjoying summer stand out as vast green terrain maps surrounded by the brilliant blue of the oceans. Patches of white cloud obscure some of the detail; other white blobs are snow and ice on mountain ranges and polar seas.

Against the blackness of the earth's night side is a gleaming spot—the space station, reflecting the light of the sun.

Two hours and fifty-four minutes after departure, we are 17,750 miles from the earth's surface. Our speed has dropped sharply, to 10,500 miles an hour. Five hours and eight minutes en route, the earth is 32,950 miles away, and our speed is 8,000 miles an hour; after twenty hours, we're 132,000 miles from the earth, traveling at 4,300 miles an hour.

On the first day, we discard the empty departure tanks. Engineers in protective suits step outside the cabin, stand for a moment in space, then make their way down the girders to the big spheres. They pump any remaining propellant into reserve tanks, disconnect the useless containers, and give them a gentle shove. For awhile the tanks drift alongside us; soon they float out of sight. Eventually they will crash on the moon.

There is no hazard for the engineers in this operation. As a precaution, they were secured to the ship by safety lines, but they could probably have done as well without them. There is no air in space to blow them away.

That's just one of the peculiarities of space to which we must adapt ourselves. Lacking a natural sequence of night and day, we live by an arbitrary time schedule. Because nothing has weight, cooking and eating are special problems. Kitchen utensils have magnetic strips or clamps so they won't float away. The heating of food is done on electronic ranges. They have many advantages: they're clean, easy to operate, and their short-wave rays don't burn up precious oxygen.

Difficulties of Dining in Space. We have no knives, spoons, or forks. All solid food is precut; all liquids are served in plastic bottles and forced directly into the mouth by squeezing. Our mess kits have spring-operated covers; our only eating utensils are tonglike devices; if we open the covers carefully, we can grab a mouthful of food without getting it all over the cabin.

From the start of the trip, the ship's crew has been maintaining a round-the-clock schedule, standing eight-hour watches. Captains, navigators, and radio-men spend most of their time checking and rechecking our flight track, ready to start up the rockets for a change of course if an error turns up. Technicians back up this operation with reports from the complex and delicate "electronic brains"—computers, gyroscopes, switchboards, and other instruments—on the control deck. Other specialists keep watch over the air-conditioning, temperature, pressure, and oxygen systems.

But the busiest crew members are the maintenance engineers and their assistants, tireless men who have been bustling back and forth between ships since
shortly after the voyage started, anxiously checking propellant tanks, tubing,
rocket motors, turbopumps, and all other vital equipment. Excessive heat could
cause dangerous hairline cracks in the rocket motors; unexpectedly large meteors could smash through the thin bumpers surrounding the propellant tanks;
fittings could come loose. The engineers have to be careful.

We are still slowing down. At the start of the fourth day, our speed has
dropped to 800 miles an hour, only slightly more than the speed of a conventional jet fighter. Ahead, the harsh surface features of the moon are clearly outlined. Behind, the blue-green ball of the earth appears to be barely a yard in
diameter.

Our fleet of unpowered rocket ships is now passing the neutral point between
the gravitational fields of the earth and the moon. Our momentum has dropped
off to almost nothing, yet we're about to pick up speed. For now we begin falling toward the moon, about 23,600 miles away. With no atmosphere to slow
us, we'll smash into the moon at 6,000 miles an hour unless we do something
about it.

Rotating the Moon Ship. This is what we do: aboard each ship, near its center
of gravity, is a positioning device consisting of three flywheels set at right angles
to one another and operated by electric motors. One of the wheels heads in the
same direction as our flight patch—in other words, along the longitudinal axis
of the vehicle, like the rear wheels of a car. Another parallels the latitudinal
axis, like the steering wheel of an ocean vessel. The third lies along the horizontal axis, like the rear steering wheel of a hook-and-ladder truck. If we start any
one of the wheels spinning, it causes our rocket ship to turn slowly in the other
direction (pilots know this "torque" effect; if increased power causes a plane's
propeller to spin more rapidly in one direction, the pilot has to fight his controls to keep the plane from rolling in the other direction).

The captain of our spaceship orders the longitudinal flywheel set in motion.
Slowly our craft begins to cartwheel; when it has turned half a revolution, it
stops. We are going toward the moon tail-end-first, a position which will enable
us to brake our fall with our rocket motors when the right time comes.

Tension increases aboard the three ships. The landing is tricky—so tricky that
it will be done entirely by automatic pilot, to diminish the possibilty of human
error. Our scientists compute our rate of descent, the spot at which we expect
to strike, the speed and direction of the moon (it's traveling at 2,280 miles
an hour at right angles to our path). These and other essential statistics are
fed into a tape. The tape, based on the same principle as the player-piano roll
and the automatic business-machine card, will control the automatic pilot. (Actually, a number of tapes intended to provide for all eventualities will be fixed

up long before the flight, but last-minute checks are necessary to see which tape to use, and to see whether a manual correction of our course is required before the autopilot takes over.)

Now we lower part of our landing gear—four spiderlike legs, hinged to the square rocket assembly, which have been folded against the framework.

As we near the end of our trip, the gravity of the moon, which is still to one side of us, begins to pull us off our elliptical course, and we turn the ship to conform to this change of direction. At an altitude of 550 miles, the rocket motors begin firing; we feel the shock of their blasts inside the personnel sphere and suddenly our weight returns. Objects which have not been secured beforehand tumble to the floor. The force of the rocket motors is such that we have about one third our normal earth weight.

The final ten minutes are especially tense. The tape-guided automatic pilots are now in full control. We fall more and more slowly, floating over the landing area like descending helicopters. As we approach, the fifth leg of our landing gear—a big telescopic shock absorber which has been housed in the center of the rocket assembly—is lowered through the fiery blast of the motors. The long green flames begin to splash against the baked lunar surface. Swirling clouds of brown-gray dust are thrown out sideways; they settle immediately, instead of hanging in air, as they would on the earth.

The broad round shoe of the telescopic landing leg digs into the soft volcanic ground. If it strikes too hard, an electronic mechanism inside it immediately calls on the rocket motors for more power to cushion the blow. For a few seconds, we balance on the single leg. Then the four outrigger legs slide out to help support the weight of the ship, and are locked into position. The whirring of machinery dies away. There is absolute silence. We have reached the moon.

* *The Principles of Interplanetary Flight*

In this article Arthur Clarke gives another discussion of some of the basic factors involved in the lunar voyage: the take-off, the method of effecting a landing, and the return to earth. It is interesting to compare this moon trip with that described by von Braun in the previous article. Although written from a different point of view the two are essentially the same except on some minor points. Various techniques have been worked out for getting to the moon and back, each of which has its champions. One point on which everyone seems agreed is that it is no good trying to launch a single mammoth rocket from the surface of the earth directly to the moon. Such a procedure raises impossible engineering problems that rule it out immediately. It is much simpler to get into space piecemeal. The process might be compared with putting a roof on a house. It is an easy matter to bring up the nails, shingles, etc., as you need them and put them in place. But it would be a tremendous task to build the roof complete on the ground and then try to hoist it on top of the house. Von Braun transports equipment from the earth and assembles his moon ships entirely in space. After assembly they are loaded with fuel and sent on their way to the moon. Arthur Clarke has three rockets leave the earth together and enter into an orbit 500 miles from the earth. Two of these rockets are tankers which refuel the third ship, which then accelerates out of its orbit until it attains sufficient velocity to reach the moon.

It is at the moon that von Braun and Arthur Clarke part company. Before landing, Clarke has his rocket ship enter into a circular orbit around the moon at an altitude of a few hundred miles, during which it detaches the fuel tanks needed for the return voyage. The rocket then descends to the surface of the moon leaving the fuel tanks orbiting in space. After completing its mission on the moon, the rocket ship matches velocity with the fuel tanks again, attaches them to it, and returns to earth. The advantage is that the ship does not have to do the work of carrying the fuel down to the surface of the moon and back out into space again, since the fuel is not needed for the landing or take-off maneuver. Keeping the fuel tanks would be something like carrying a heavy knapsack of food up and down a hill when you don't intend to eat until later anyhow. You can save yourself some work by leaving the knapsack at the bottom. Von Braun does not mention orbital refueling but has his ships land directly on the moon with all their fuel intact. Perhaps he felt the fuel saved would not be worth the time required to execute this maneuver. Also, perhaps we should not attempt the moon trip at all unless we have so much fuel available that it is not necessary to resort to such economy measures.

Doubtless many of our ideas about going to the moon will be outmoded before they even have a chance to be put into practice. But the basic principles involved will still hold. They will be just as good a thousand years from now as they are today.

✳

The Earth-Moon Journey

ARTHUR C. CLARKE

VELOCITY *Requirements.* The simplest of all journeys into space, and the first which will be actually accomplished, is the journey to or around the moon, which will now be considered in detail. The conclusions reached in this chapter will apply, it should be noted, both to guided missiles, uncontrolled projectiles, or manned spaceships. They must all obey the same fundamental laws.

As far as energy requirements are concerned, Figure 1 shows that the moon is, dynamically speaking, very nearly at "infinity," despite its astronomical nearness. It needs a velocity of 11.2 kilometers per second to project a body to infinity—and 11.1 km/sec to project it so that it just reaches the moon (385,000 km. or 240,000 miles at mean distance). This velocity difference is so small that it is frequently ignored and it is assumed that the full escape velocity is needed for the mission.

A body leaving the earth in the direction of the moon would be subject to the gravitational field of both bodies, but for three quarters of the way, that of the moon is completely negligible, as is shown in Figure 2. This diagram gives the accelerations produced by earth and moon cm/sec^2: in order to show the values over the region where both are significant, the scale here has been multiplied by 100.

Arthur C. Clarke, from *Interplanetary Flight,* Temple Press, Chapter V.

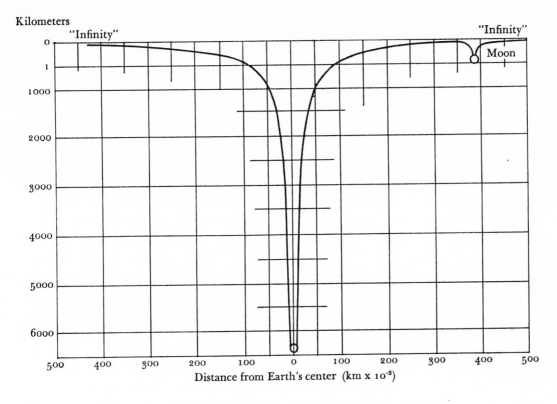

Figure 1. Potential Energy Diagram of Earth-Moon System.

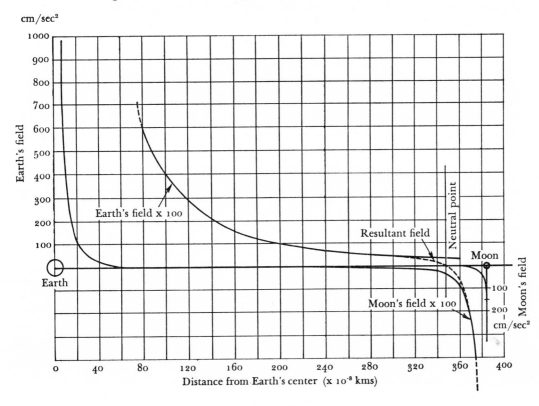

Figure 2. Gravitational Fields of Earth and Moon.

Since the fields are opposing, they have been drawn on opposite sides of the horizontal axis, and it will be seen that there is a point—the so-called neutral point—at which both fields are equal and the resultant (represented by the dotted line) vanishes. Up to this point, the body would have an acceleration toward the earth: thereafter, the force acting upon it would be directed to the moon. It might be mentioned here that, contrary to the vivid descriptions given by many writers, absolutely *no* physical phenomena of any kind would take place in a rocket passing this point. Since the machine would be in a "free fall," with only gravitational forces acting upon it, its occupants would be weightless and so would be quite unaware of the fact that the actual direction of fall had altered. Nor would it be possible for a body with insufficient speed to be stranded at the neutral point: the equilibrium would be quite unstable owing to the movement of the moon and the (very small) perturbations produced by the sun and planets.

As it receded from the earth, the rocket's velocity would decrease and it would thus pass the neutral point at a speed of about 1.6 km/sec in its fall toward the moon. The moon's escape velocity is 2.34 km/sec, and this is the speed with which the rocket, if it started from rest at a great distance, would crash into the moon's surface. In the case we have taken, the rocket has a certain additional energy since it left earth with a speed slightly in excess of minimum requirements. Allowing for this, we find that in the fall toward the moon the rocket would reach a terminal speed of about 2.8 km/sec (6,300 m.p.h.). Clearly, if a safe landing is to be made, this speed must be neutralized by the further application of rocket power.

Obviously this is not quite the most economical journey to the moon, as the spaceship did not crawl past the neutral point but went through it at an appreciable speed—in other words, it started with more than the minimum velocity needed for the mission. This excess speed carried over from the original take-off would increase the difficulty of the lunar landing, and a small saving would be made if the rocket left earth with barely enough speed to reach the neutral point. The initial velocity would then be 11.1 instead of 11.2 km/sec, and it would reach the moon at 2.34 instead of 2.8 km/sec—a total reduction of, surprisingly enough, as much as 0.6 km/sec for the mission.

There is an infinite number of possible trajectories to the moon, according to the initial velocity and direction of the rocket when leaving the earth: but in every case it must reach the moon at a speed of not less than 2.34 km/sec unless some form of braking is employed. To return again to the analogy of the two adjacent valleys in Figure 1, this is the speed which the rocket will acquire in falling into the upper of the two pits if it has just sufficient energy to surmount the "hump" between them.

If the rocket was not falling directly toward the moon, but *past* it, then it would go round our satellite in an approximately parabolic or hyperbolic orbit and in certain cases might return to earth. The exact shape of the orbits near the moon is very sensitive to small changes in the initial velocity and direction: according to Kooy and Uytenbogaart* all the possible "return" orbits lie within a speed range of only 1 per cent at the projection point, i.e. between about 11.1 and 11.2 km/sec. Below 11.1 km/sec it would be impossible to reach the moon; above 11.2 km/sec the body would be traveling too fast when it passed the moon for our satellite to deflect it back to earth.

Just as the earth has its characteristic circular velocity of about 8 km/sec, so has the moon, the value for a point near its surface being 1.65 km/sec (equivalent to a period of 1.8 hours). It may seem a little odd to speak of satellites of satellites, but from the point of view of the sun this is what the moon already is! If, therefore, when a rocket was falling past the moon, its speed was reduced to the appropriate value by firing its motors in the direction of flight, then it might continue to circle our satellite, perhaps taking observations automatically and radioing them back to earth. If the fuel reserves were sufficient, it might at a later time be accelerated again into an orbit which would return it to our planet. The velocities on the return journey would be identical with those on the outward one: the rocket would cross the neutral point at its minimum speed, and then accelerate more and more rapidly until it reached the earth at 11.1 km/sec—the speed with which it originally started.

It will be seen, therefore, that as soon as it becomes possible to build rockets which can escape from the earth at all, a considerable range of interesting possibilities will be opened up. The payloads of the first "parabolic" rockets will be only a few kilograms and they will herald their arrival on the moon by the flash they produce in our telescopes. According to Goddard, less than three pounds of flash powder would cause an explosion easily visible in quite a small instrument. Later it will be possible to employ considerably larger payloads, and lightweight radio transmitters, relaying the information obtained by arrays of recording instruments, will be installed. Finally, it will be possible to use television to obtain close-ups of the moon, and, in particular, of its far side which can never be seen from earth.

These later developments will require improvements in telemetering and telecontrol equipment almost as great as in rocket motor design, but do not demand anything essentially novel. It may safely be assumed** that propulsion and guiding techniques will advance together, and that when we can build a rocket capable of reaching the moon, we will also be able to control it at that point.

The above discussion leads us to the conception of the "characteristic velocity" which a rocket needs if it is to carry out any particular mission. For a

---

* *Ballistics of the Future*, p. 457.

** Even by the disheartened rocket engineer who made the celebrated remark, "The trouble with guided missiles is that there aren't any."

rocket which is required to reach the moon, but may be allowed to crash on it unchecked or shoot past it into space, this velocity, as we have seen, is 11.1 km/sec, or a little less than the velocity of escape. If it is desired to make a landing to set down instruments or, later, human beings, then the machine's fall into the moon's field must be counteracted. This means that in some way the rocket must be reorientated in space so that its motors point toward the moon, and rocket braking must be employed. To put it picturesquely, the rocket must "sit on its exhaust" and so descend slowly onto our satellite's surface.

If this maneuver was carried out in the most economical manner possible, it would require the combustion of exactly as much fuel as the *escape* from the moon. Both missions are identical apart from the change in sign: it requires just as much energy to accelerate in space as to decelerate. The moon's escape velocity being 2.34 km/sec, the characteristic velocity for the whole trip is 11.1 plus 2.34 or 13.44 km/sec. The rocket must therefore be designed as if it had to reach this speed. . . .

Mass-Ratio Requirements. This figure of nearly 13.5 km/sec is a theoretical minimum value: it does not allow for gravitational loss at the take-off from earth and an exactly corresponding, though much smaller, loss at the lunar landing. Taking these factors into account, the characteristic velocity for a voyage from rest on the earth's surface to rest on the moon's is about 16 km/sec (36,000 m.p.h.) With the most powerful chemical fuels ever likely to be available this would require an effective mass-ratio of about 35 and hence would involve the use of rockets of at least three stages, or else orbital refueling techniques.

For a return journey, the characteristic velocity must be doubled: it would therefore be about 32 km/sec. However, an interesting and important complication arises here. The descent onto the moon could only be carried out by rocket braking, since there is practically no atmosphere. In the case of the earth, the final landing could certainly be by parachute or some equivalent aerodynamic means. Indeed, it is possible that the greater part of the 11.1 km/sec which the rocket would acquire on its long fall back from the neutral point could be destroyed by air resistance, by the technique of "braking ellipses."

This procedure was worked out in great detail by the early German writers and is as follows. Suppose that in its fall toward the earth the rocket is aimed so that it passes through the highest levels of the atmosphere—at an altitude of about 100 kilometers. It will suffer a certain amount of retardation due to air resistance, which, if the altitude is chosen correctly, can be of any desired value. (There would be no great danger of the rocket becoming incandescent at these altitudes, for it would have only one fifth of the speed of a meteor at this level and the air resistance would therefore be only a twenty-fifth as great.) After "grazing" the atmosphere, the rocket would again emerge into space, where the frictional heating produced on its walls could be lost by radiation. It would now, however, be traveling at a speed substantially less than escape velocity, and so after receding from earth to a considerable distance would return again along a very elongated ellipse. At perigee it would re-enter the atmosphere, cutting through it at a lower level but at less speed than on the first contact.

In this way, after a series of diminishing ellipses, the rocket could shed most of its excess speed without using any fuel. Indeed, it has been calculated that the entire landing on the earth could be carried out in this manner, the final "touchdown" being by parachute. Before this can be settled definitely, much more extensive knowledge of the upper atmosphere will be required, but undoubtedly substantial savings of fuel can be effected in this way.

Taking the most optimistic view we can calculate the characteristic velocity for the round trip as follows:

	THEORETICAL MINIMUM	ALLOWING FOR "G-LOSS"
Escape from earth	11.1	12.5
Landing on moon	2.34	3.0
Take-off from moon	2.34	3.0
Navigational corrections	—	0.5
	15.78 km/sec	19.0 km/sec

The more pessimistic estimate, which assumes that the whole of the landing on earth would have to be done by rocket braking, would be about 32 km/sec.

These performances would demand effective mass-ratios of about 70 and 1,000 respectively with the best conceivable chemical fuels, from which it will be seen what an important role air-braking can play if it proves practicable. But even the lower figure of 70 would require, for a ship large enough to carry men and their equipment, an initial mass of many thousand tons at take-off. This demonstrates once again the virtual impossibility of a return voyage to the moon, with landing, in a chemically-propelled rocket.

The economics of the earth-moon voyage would, however, alter drastically if orbital refueling was employed. There are many ways in which this might be done, and a recent scheme* will be described as an example of one such method.

Instead of launching a single mammoth rocket, which might have to weigh 20,000 tons or so, *three* rockets, each of about 600 tons mass, would take off simultaneously and enter an orbit 500 miles from the earth. Two would merely act as "tankers" and would refuel the third, which would then accelerate out of its orbit and travel toward the moon. On reaching the vicinity of the moon, it would enter a circular orbit around our satellite at an altitude of a few hun-

* H. E. Ross, "Orbital Bases," from *Journal of the British Interplanetary Society*, Vol. 8, Nos. 4-7, January, 1949.

dred miles, *and would here detach the fuel tanks needed for the return journey.* These would be left circling the moon while the ship descended to the surface.

When it took off again, it would rendezvous onto the still orbiting fuel tanks, reattach them, and make the return journey to earth. The beauty of this scheme —which could have several other variations—is that no unnecessary work would be done, and hence a vast saving in over-all weight could be effected. Instead of carrying the fuel for the return journey and final earth landing down to the moon and up again, it would be left in space where it could be collected on the homeward voyage. This would save decelerating several tons of fuel from 2 km/sec down to zero and re-accelerating it from zero up to 2 km/sec again.

The technical difficulties involved in this sort of maneuver would of course be considerable, and a single mistake at any stage might be fatal. But it must be remembered that once a body is set circling in an orbit, its position for many years ahead can be predicted with great accuracy, so the location of the fuel "caches" would always be known with precision. Moreover, the very smallest of radio beacons would enable them to be located at a range of thousands of miles in free space.

It must also be realized that such an enterprise would not be carried out *de novo,* but only after a long period of experimentation when earlier expeditions had made numerous circumnavigations of the moon and perhaps already established orbital fuel reserves.

The main assumption in such schemes as this is that the problems of navigation and control of large rockets will be solved as completely as for aircraft, and there seems no reason to suppose that this will not be the case.

Transit Times. So far, no mention has been made of the duration of the lunar journey. If the rocket maintained its initial speed of 11 km/sec (25,000 m.p.h.) it would reach the moon after ten hours, but since its velocity is steadily decreasing the figure is considerably greater. For a body leaving the earth's neighborhood at the minimum speed which enables it to reach the moon at all (11.1 km/sec), the journey to the moon's orbit takes about 116 hours. This, however, ignores the acceleration of the moon's field toward the end of the journey, which would produce a small but appreciable reduction of transit time.

This figure of 116 hours is therefore the *maximum* length of time a free projectile could take on the direct journey to the moon. A rocket which had to engage in retarding maneuvers would, of course, be longer on the journey.

Five days is not a great deal of time in which to make a voyage to another world* and it would decrease very sharply if the rocket left the earth with any appreciable excess speed over the minimum of 11.1 km/sec. Some typical values for these transit times are tabulated below.

---

* It compares quite favorably with the ten weeks of Columbus's first voyage!

Transit Times to the Moon

| INITIAL VELOCITY | TRANSIT TIME |
MILES/SEC	HOURS
6.88	116
6.94	49
7.56	19
8.18	14
8.80	11
9.42	10
10.04	8
13.14	6

These figures have been calculated for the mean distance of the moon—385,000 km. or 240,000 miles—and would vary somewhat from time to time as the moon's distance alters slightly: but they give a good idea of the order of duration of the journey under various conditions. The fact that doubling the initial speed reduces the transit time to a twentieth is certainly surprising, and is a good example of the danger of relying on ordinary terrestrial ideas of transport when discussing astronautics. However, speeds of 20 km/sec will still remain of purely theoretical interest for a long time after lunar journeys have become commonplace, and the early explorers will no doubt prefer fairly leisurely journeys to give them ample time to check their position and carry out their somewhat intricate braking maneuvers.

But no doubt in due course the survivors of the first generation of astronauts will shake their heads over the modern craze for speed, when the five days that was good enough for them begins to be carved down to five hours.

* *Landing on the Moon*

As we come nearer to solving the problem of sending manned vessels to the moon, the question of where to land grows steadily more acute. All sorts of factors enter into consideration, such as the temperature of the surface, the number of interesting features within a short radius, and the smoothness of the surface. We can easily find a zone where a moderate temperature prevails at noonday, by settling in a belt that is a calculable distance from the region where the sun is directly overhead. From scanning the features in this zone one can select a spot where a variety of interesting formations are concentrated within a small area. Trying to find a good landing site, however, is not nearly so easy. Areas that look smooth may actually be quite rough. There would seem to be no way of solving the landing problem in advance. Even our most powerful telescopes are incapable of distinguishing between an area that appears smooth and one that is really smooth. Also, we have no assurance that the ground is solid underneath. It may be porous and unable to support the legs of a landing vehicle. As the author emphasizes, it appears that a landing site can only be selected from observations made on the spot a few miles above the surface.

*

Where To Land on the Moon

H. PERCY WILKINS

THE time is approaching when men will first visit the moon. Many and varied problems connected with the first lunar journey have received attention from writers; the space platform, the vehicle, oxidant and fuel, and so on, have each come under review, but very little attention has been given to the actual landing sites.

The object of the venture being to effect a landing on the moon, it is evident

H. Percy Wilkins, from *Journal of the British Interplanetary Society*, Vol. 13, No. 2, March, 1954.

that not only must the vehicle be provided with means for settling down without undue shock, and in a suitable position for the take-off, but some attention must be given to find the most suitable landing sites on the surface of our satellite. This is not as simple as it seems, for it presupposes a knowledge of the nature of the lunar surface, not in its broad and general aspect, whether it is mountainous or level, but in the minute features. Before approving the selection of a site, it is important to know whether the spot on which the vehicle will settle is a level expanse of rock capable of bearing the weight, or whether a deceptive layer of dust conceals crevasses or other irregularities in the solid surface beneath. If the latter happened to be the case we can visualize one or more of the "landing legs" plunging through the dust and into the cracks with disastrous results to both vehicle and crew.

The selection of landing sites presents two problems. Possible sites must be located in the most advantageous spots for exploration and easily reached from each other and it must be established that within the sites, the areas selected for the actual landings are suitable for this somewhat delicate operation.

On the side of the moon which faces the earth the southern portion is, in general, mountainous while on the northern portion are found the extensive and comparatively level plains, misnamed "seas." Within the mountainous area the only possible sites are the interiors of certain of the great craterform features or walled plains. Many of these exhibit rough and disturbed interiors and can be discarded as quite unsuitable for our purpose. The only apparently level expanses in this region are the interiors of Stofler, Schomberger, Pontecoul, and Schickard.

At mean libration, the center of the disk lies near the middle of the small plain known as Sinus Medii, on the southern border of which is the great walled plain Ptolemy [Plate XIIIa], 90 miles in diameter. Both Sinus Medii and Ptolemy are possible landing sites.

On the north, we have such objects as Archimedes, Plato, and Meton, with Endymion to the west and Otto Struve to the east. The extensive seas are too open to be considered as really suitable sites. Why land on a congealed lava flow miles from any object of interest?

These possible landing sites can be found on the end-paper maps and it will be noted that they are well distributed and very approximately equidistant from each other. Those near the apparent edge or limb are suitable for exploration of the moon's other side.

It remains to inquire whether the surfaces of these otherwise favorable spots are suitable for landing. This is a matter for direct observation with very large telescopes, which alone are capable of revealing the nature of the ground. We realize that what to us on the earth seem insignificant irregularities may be formidable hazards to the crew of a spaceship.

Up to the present time, large instruments have rarely been employed for lunar observations, the only systematic series of lunar observations being those of the writer and Patrick Moore with the 33-inch and 25-inch refractors at Meudon and Cambridge observatories respectively.

In general, the larger the telescope and the better the seeing, the more rough does the moon's surface appear. Objects which seem nearly or quite smooth in small telescopes are transformed into undulating, much pitted and fissured expanses in large instruments. Where fissures exist, the sharpness of their edges clearly proves that those regions have no covering of dust, the actual rocky surface being exposed.

The existence of large numbers of pits of considerable depth is also incompatible with a mantle of dust of sufficient thickness as to approach leveling up of the surface. Some objects are very bright, others are very dark and the confusion of pits and cracks is more evident in the brighter than in the darker ones. It is not entirely a matter of easier detection of detail in bright objects, for some dark spots are altogether rough and warty.

It must be remembered that the smallest object visible in even the largest telescopes must be a couple of hundred yards across, that is, of equal size to a landing site. In other words a landing site would appear as a mere dot in the finest instruments. In examining various objects on the moon with a view to establishing their suitability as landing sites I have looked for such bright dots, and where one has been seen, have assumed that it indicates an uneven and unsuitable area.

In every object critically examined such indications have been detected, separated by expanses which seem perfectly smooth but which, in all probability, actually contain pits and cracks too small for telescopic detection. *The entire surface of the moon, even in the apparently perfectly smooth regions, is probably so rough and uneven as to make landing a matter of selectivity on the part of space travelers.* No evidence has been found for extensive dust deposits, the apparent surface being the true and solid crust of the moon.

From a consideration of the translucent appearance of some of the lighter regions, notably that of the Palus Somnii, and the remarkable apparent variations in certain areas during the course of a lunar day, it is very possible that a good deal of the surface layer is itself of a brittle nature, with numerous cavities below the surface. Although probably only a few inches across and a few inches below the surface, the presence of great numbers of such hollows renders the surface incapable of sustaining any appreciable weight and therefore unsuitable and unsafe for landings.

The conclusion seems to be that the most suitable landing sites are the darker portions of the objects charted, which are themselves remarkably smooth in comparison with the majority of lunar formations. A safe landing can probably be effected on a dark area between adjacent brighter spots, but the actual degree of smoothness can only be determined when within a few miles of the surface.

* *The Exploration*

In the excitement of going to the moon we must not lose sight of one all-important fact: what to do after we get there. People often seem to feel that the wonder of treading on another world would be so overpowering that the men would wander about in a kind of daze, exclaiming over the different marvels that confront them. On the contrary, landing on a world such as the moon or Mars would probably seem no more wonderful than being set down in a space suit on a particularly barren stretch of the Arizona desert. If all the preparation and expense that went into the trip are to be justified, the first explorers of the moon will be very busy people indeed. Each man will have a definite assignment that will keep him busy every moment up to take-off. The men will not only be working under great pressure but under considerable tension due to the hazardous nature of lunar conditions. Discount the danger from meteorites as we will, the fact remains that one the size of a bullet *could* zip through you at any time. And if some of the men *were* killed by meteorites, it would be bound to affect the morale of the rest of the expedition. The men would doubtless go about their tasks as planned. But they would feel as if they were under fire from snipers without having any way of retaliating or protecting themselves.

Assuming the danger from meteorites turns out to be very slight, however, the men would be exceedingly busy carrying out various experiments, as well as gathering data for the benefit of future expeditions. If the first trip to the moon goes without mishap it will certainly be the greatest technological achievement of mankind, one hard to surpass for many years to come.

*

Man on the Moon—The Exploration

FRED L. WHIPPLE AND WERNHER VON BRAUN

THERE is danger on the moon—the danger of the unknown. Our first expedition, which can land there in the next twenty-five years, must be prepared. Tissue-damaging cosmic rays—invisible, deep-penetrating atom particles—unpredictably streak in from space, with no atmosphere to impede them. Meteorites, from microscopic grains to mountainous boulders, hurtle down. On the lunar surface, thin layers of crust might cover great crevasses, making travel perilous. Jagged rocks threaten the fabric of the pressurized, oxygen-equipped space suits essential to life.

How great are the hazards? We don't know exactly, but we do know how to take precautions. Until we can measure the severity of the cosmic radiation, we shall stay under cover as much as possible. Our headquarters must be located in a deep crack in the surface, protected from both rays and meteorites. Brief exposure to cosmic radiation probably won't hurt us. Exposure to large meteorites will hurt us, but we don't expect to encounter them; the smaller meteorites will shatter against the two thicknesses of our space suits. The keen eyes of experienced geologists will guard us against breakthroughs in the crust. Caution should be ample protection against rips in the precious space suits. We can explore the moon safely.

Our first step after arrival is to unload equipment and prepare for a six-week stay. Three awkward-looking but efficient rocket ships (none of them streamlined, because there is no air resistance in space) have carried us to the lunar surface from a man-made satellite 1,075 miles above the earth. On this voyage, two of the craft carried passengers and propellant for a return trip; the third, a one-way cargo vehicle, must be dismantled and converted into living and working quarters for the fifty-man expedition.

We have arrived just at the beginning of the two weeks of sunlight that comprise the lunar day. From the catwalks of the ships, 130 feet above the moon's surface, the scene is dismal. The pitted surface of the landing area—a place known to scientists as Sinus Roris, or "Dewy Bay" [Plate VIII], not far from the

Fred L. Whipple and Wernher von Braun, from *Collier's*, October 25, 1952.

lunar north pole—stretches to the south like a vast, discolored expanse of broken ice.

On the other three sides, we are surrounded by towering mountains. The rays of the rising sun have painted the great mountain range a blinding white against the pitch blackness of the sky. But elsewhere, there is none of the brilliant color we are used to on earth—just dull, lifeless browns and grays. There is no cloud cover, no wind, no rain or snow—no weather of any kind. Overhead, pinpoint stars shine steadily; they don't twinkle, for there is no blurring atmosphere, as on earth.

Dust-covered, drab, silent, the panorama has the frozen stillness of a faded backdrop.

From our headquarters site we can explore any place within a range of 250 miles, and all the lunar features of interest to our scientists fall within that area. It may require some long trips, though—the region involved is approximately as large as the whole northeastern part of the United States, north of Washington, D. C.; in other words, the size of the six New England states, New York, Pennsylvania, New Jersey, Maryland, and Delaware. Besides looking over selected sites on the side of the moon visible from the earth, we'll also be able to see a part of the unknown side, the part always turned away from the earth.

What will we be looking for?

To start with, our scientists want to know whether any faint traces of atmosphere are present, what minerals there are (maybe we'll find some rare, useful ones), whether the moon has a magnetic field like the earth, and how the temperature varies beneath the lunar crust. Sheer curiosity suggests other questions and will play a large part in our explorations. We're the first people who've ever been here, the first ever to peer into the mysterious lunar valleys, the first to examine the mountains and craters of the moon close up. Who knows what we may find on this virgin ball of unexplored rock, about five times the size of the United States?

But the principal aim of our expedition during this first lunar exploration will be strictly scientific, and very important. Our investigations will help us unravel the secret of the universe: how the moon and planets were born and what they're made of. Up to now, all our information on that subject has come from examination of the earth and from surveying the heavens from observatories. The moon will give us a new perspective: a different look at the astral bodies and the story of its own birth as a clue to the birth of other satellites, planets, and stars.

We know that the moon didn't form in the Pacific Ocean and get hurled into space, as was generally believed fifty years ago. It *is* possible that it was an independent planet which came from outer space, fell into the earth's gravitational field, smashed into the Pacific and then ricocheted back into its present orbit. But the most likely explanation is that the moon originally consisted of a belt of gases and minerals that girdled the earth—much as Saturn's ring surrounds that planet today—and eventually fused into a solid mass.

That's the theory we'll check.

First, if there are faint traces of such heavy gases as xenon and krypton, we'll know the moon was never a completely molten, hot mass (for extreme heat would have dispelled *all* gases), and so could not have been an independent planet. We'll find out by using a rotary pump which will compress whatever gases may exist and capture them in a bottlelike container. It probably will take many days to accumulate enough of whatever gases there may be, but checking them will be fairly simple.

Does the Moon Have an Iron Core? Then we'll look for a magnetic field. If we don't find it, we'll have another indication that the moon doesn't have an iron core, as an independent planet would. Compasslike magnetometers will do the trick for us; if the moon has magnetic poles as the earth has, they will show up (isolated iron deposits also will register, but they will be easily distinguished from a core).

We'll also shake up the moon's surface a bit. Scientists have learned a lot about the earth from earthquakes. The vibration waves of a quake travel freely through solids—which is how we know that the center of the earth is molten iron. We can't count on having moonquakes, so we'll make some: we'll send off rockets with high-explosive war heads and then read the story of the waves from our seismographs. The explosions occurring about 100 miles away will show if the moon's core is molten (in which case, our waves will be stopped), solid (they'll go right through), or a jumble of rocks which never have been molten (muffled waves).

There is another clue to the moon's origin: the scars on its surface. The plains of the moon are rough and scored by fissures. Close examination will disclose whether these score marks are cracks or wrinkles. Wrinkles will indicate that the moon was molten at birth, and has cooled since. Cracks will be evidence that it was cool to begin with and has since been heated, perhaps by radioactivity. Fortunately, these lunar birthmarks have not been washed away by erosion, as has happened on the earth.

So much for the moon's past. There are also some facts we want to learn about its present. One of the most important is the exact intensity of the cosmic rays which strike it. As soon as we're settled in our quarters, we set out instruments to measure the rays. Another is the frequency of meteorite hits. Careful measurements also will be kept of the surface temperature caused by the sun, and we'll want to measure the subsurface temperature at varying depths (it may be considerably warmer than the surface, due to radioactivity).

For two weeks, we devote ourselves to research on these points, past and present. The expedition breaks up into teams, each with its own assignment.

Most of the investigating during this period is done within a 10-mile radius of the base. It's difficult, dangerous work. We climb across meteor pits, into chasms, up great rock piles, struggling in our bulky suits, always fearful of snagging ourselves on sharp outcroppings, always nervous about stray meteorites and watchful for thin crust.

Because we'll never be really certain how safe we are on the moon, however long we stay, we keep up a chatter over our walkie-talkie radio transmitters, not to bolster our courage, but for a practical reason: if something happens to us, the people back at headquarters will have a record of our findings.

For the same reason, lunar headquarters maintains constant contact with the earth. Back there, a special panel of scientists remains in constant session, as it will all during out six-week stay. A dozen specialists in fields like astronomy, astrophysics, geophysics, mineralogy, and geology follow our every move by radio (as, indeed, does the entire world), keeping track of our findings, suggesting new leads and occasionally asking for the repetition of an experiment. Television transmission is impractical, but every day dozens of photographs are radioed back to earth.

For those on the moon, the work is endless and fascinating. We collect samples of everything in sight—dust (where did it come from; what's it composed of?), mineral specimens, rock and lava fragments. Besides scouring the lunar surface, we make test drillings several hundred feet into the moon's ground, and collect more samples that way.

We work in almost frantic haste during these two weeks, trying to make the most of the brilliant sunlight. We eat and sleep in shifts, so that there will be no halt in the research, no break in the flow of information back to the earth.

But soon the sun begins to slip over the horizon. For a while, there's plenty of light; work slows down but not entirely. For several days after sunset, we live in a kind of twilight, with a cold, but fairly bright, illumination cast over us by the earth (it reflects about 60 times as much sunlight on the moon as the full moon reflects on the earth). The browns and grays of the lunar day take on a green tint; mountains throw long shadows; craters and chasms appear jet black. The light grows dimmer as the "full earth" becomes a "half earth."

Now comes an exciting moment: the start of our longest expedition. We've had to wait to make it, because all the vehicles have been in constant use for the vital explorations near the base; as a result, we'll have to travel outbound in comparative darkness. That's not desirable, but it's possible, and we have no alternative.

Our destination is a crater about 195 miles away as the rocket flies, but about 250 miles off by lunar tractor. This crater, called Harpalus [Plate VIII], is the most interesting one within reach—24 miles across, with a surrounding ridge 3,100 feet high, and a depth of almost 11,000 feet from peak to bottom.

It must have taken a monstrous meteorite to smash into the moon with such force—or was it a meteorite? That's one of the questions we want answered. All we know before we start is that a meteorite *could* make such a crater, if it were the size of a small mountain, and traveling at a speed of thousands of miles an hour. Another mystery we can solve on this journey is the nature of the great white marks which radiate for tremendous distances from the most perfect (and perhaps the newest) craters. Maybe they're powdered dust, shot out by the impact of a meteorite against the moon; maybe their origin is volcanic. We'll soon know.

Our expedition consists of two tractors, hauling three trailers each. Ten men are making the trip, and we carry supplies and fuel enough to last about two weeks. The outbound trip should take a little less than five days, the return journey, made in sunlight, perhaps four; we also want to spend a day or two at the crater. That's ten days. We carry an extra four days' emergency supplies.

The trip is slow and difficult. The two vehicles cautiously pick their way around great rocks and deep pits, making about two miles an hour over the rough ground. Powerful searchlights and radar probe for major obstacles; at suspicious places, a geologist hops out to scan the ground for thin crust and feel his way afoot. When, despite our precautions, one of the tractors gets stuck in a rut, the other hauls it out.

At selected points along our course, we stop and plant explosives—part of our vibration-wave experimentation—which technicians back at headquarters will fire later by remote control (the explosions will be visible from the earth through strong telescopes).

After four days, the perimeter ridge of Harpalus looms ahead. As we press on, the first rays of the sun, marking our second lunar day on the satellite, glare off the side of the ridge and the mountain range to our left. By the time we get to the base of the ridge, full sunlight pours down on us again.

From a few miles away, the crater rim is measured with surveying instruments and photographed with special cameras. As we move closer, lava samples are collected, and holes are drilled for additional specimens. Other members of the expedition take temperature readings, check for magnetism, and gather dust specimens.

Scaling the crater wall is a hard job. In some places, where the ridge is rough, we can make slow progress with regular mountain-climbing equipment; elsewhere, steep walls compel us to shoot grappling hooks up the sides by means of rockets; rope ladders then enable us to reach the rim. The party descends as far as it can into the mouth of the crater. When no further progress is possible, we lower one man by rope to examine the floor and gather lava specimens. It's tricky, dangerous work; despite the relatively slight gravitational pull, a tumble would be just as dangerous as on earth, for there's no atmosphere to retard a falling body.

We work swiftly, for our time is limited. After a day or two at the crater, we start back, making a detour to examine the mountain range to the northeast, where there are interesting rock and lava formations and cavelike holes of unknown origin. The trip home is faster than the journey to the crater; the vehicles are heavily laden with specimens, but there is light to drive by. In a few days, we're back at the headquarters crevice.

Now the six hectic weeks of exploration draw to a close. At the landing site, electronic engineers set up automatic recording instruments which will radio scientific observations to earth after we've taken off. These stations (not much larger than an office desk) house delicate instruments which record cosmic radiations, tremors caused by the impact of meteorites hitting the surface, temperature changes, and other scientific data. They are connected by cables to the skeleton of the cargo ship, which we're leaving behind. The ship's solar mirror generates power for the instruments, and the dishlike antenna will flash the readings to earth. Unless these automatic stations are destroyed by meteorites, they will operate for years without human supervision.

Engineers and technicians clamber over the passenger ships, checking pumps, rocket motors, and electrical connections. The day before take-off, specimens for later study, oxygen, and any remaining food are loaded onto the trailers at the lunar base. The entrances to the two huts are left open, permitting the synthetic atmosphere to escape; all material in the living quarters and laboratory will now be preserved by the vacuum of space.

During the next few hours, the cranes of the two ships haul up supplies. Each lunar tractor, when finally unloaded, is parked beside the skeleton of the cargo ship, to remain until the next lunar expedition. At last the cranes complete the loading of equipment and start hoisting men up to the catwalks of the two rocket ships. Then the cranes are folded against the framework, ready for flight.

Through the intercom, the commander of the fleet counts off the seconds to take-off. At X minus 4 seconds, a thunderous rumble sounds in the passenger spheres: the rocket motors have been started. The turbopumps are switched on, forcing hydrazine and nitric acid into the motors.

One by one, the ships slowly lift from the surface. An automatic pilot performs the complicated take-off maneuvering which will set us precisely on course for the space station circling the earth 239,000 miles away. We have timed our departure so that we shall arrive at the space station at the precise moment when its orbit is lined up with the direction of our travel.

Immediately after leaving ground, the ship's four spiderlike corner legs are jettisoned to save weight. Soon afterward, the central shock-absorbing leg is burned away by the fierce heat of the rocket motors around it.

By now, our earth weight has returned and we feel astonishingly heavy. As the ship picks up speed, we are made heavier and heavier by the force of acceleration, until at an altitude of 1,000 miles from the moon, about 2½ minutes after take-off, we weigh 3½ times normal earth weight.

We have reached maximum powered speed at this point: 4,200 miles an hour, sufficient to counteract the moon's gravitational pull and its 2,280-mile-an-hour speed in its course around the earth. We can now cut our motors; momentum will carry us beyond the moon's gravity, and from that point on we'll simply fall to our destination. As the flame of the rocket motors dies away, we become weightless once again.

From here on the flight is routine. The navigators keep constant check on our flight path (we can change course by using our rockets), fixing the position of the ships in relation to star constellations and the steadily growing globe of the earth. Far behind us, and to the right, the moon becomes correspondingly smaller.

Once past the neutral point between the gravitational fields of the moon and the earth, we start our fall, picking up speed constantly. At a distance of 131,000 miles from the space station's orbit with twenty hours of travel to go, we hit a speed of 4,300 miles an hour. Eighteen hours later, a little less than 17,000 miles from the orbit, our speed reaches 10,500 miles an hour, and we start to think about slowing down. We cartwheel our ship (by using a flywheel which, turning in one direction, causes the ship to turn in the other), so the rocket motors point toward the space station. Now we match our speed carefully. Ahead, the man-made satellite, looking like a bright star, is traveling around the earth at 15,840 miles an hour. When our speed reaches 22,200 miles an hour, we turn on the motors. Because they point in the direction of our movement, they act as brakes.

Gradually we slow down. As we get closer, we cut the motors to half power. The needle of the speed indicator backs across the dial. When it hits 15,840, our motors are off. We are now a satellite of the earth, traveling in the 1,075-mile-high orbit at just the right speed to counteract the earth's gravity. A few miles away is the space station, endlessly circling the earth at the same speed.

We are back at our starting point. Man's first exploration of the moon has ended. Space taxis speed toward us from the station. Other men pour out of the satellite's air lock to greet us.

Our next trip will be a short one: two hours to the earth, aboard one of the sleek rockets parked near-by. There, the members of our scientific panel await us—and, without question, a great crowd of earthlings, come to see the first men ever to set foot on the ancient, mysterious soil of the earth's closest neighbor in the heavens.

LIVING ON THE MOON

*

* Light Without Air

Viewing the moon through a telescope when it is at the crescent or quarter phase we cannot help being strongly impressed by the shadows on its surface. Since there is no atmosphere to diffuse the light these shadows are jet black and sharply defined. Often the wall of a crater stands out brilliantly in the sunlight while its interior is completely in shadow. Because the interiors look so black we get an entirely false idea of their depth. This probably accounts in part at least for the vitality of the theory that the craters are old volcanoes. When filled with shadow they certainly look like deep holes in the lunar surface. Not until near full moon when we see the craters under flat lighting do we get a picture of their true dimensions. Then we see that instead of being deep holes they are really very shallow structures with no resemblance to terrestrial volcanoes. Terrestrial volcanoes are mostly cone-shaped with steep walls sloping up to a small hole in the center. The lunar craters are shaped more like a pie tin. Some of the craters are so large that if we stood in the center the surrounding wall would be out of sight below the horizon. Some very small craterlets on the moon may be real volcano cones. It would be surprising if there had never been any volcanism whatever on the moon. But the major craters undoubtedly had an entirely different origin as indicated in previous articles in this book.

The shadows creeping over the surface of the moon follow a regular pattern with only minor variations from month to month. An observer stationed on the rim of Plato would see the same long pointed shadows crawling over the crater floor with monotonous regularity. Thus if we were on the moon, the shadows there would play a much more important part in our existence than they do upon the earth. Shadows on the earth are far from black since considerable light is diffused into them by atmospheric scattering, while air currents tend to equalize the temperature between regions of light and shade. In high mountains where the air is thinner, however, the difference in temperature between sunshine and shadow is more marked. On the moon where there is no air whatever, stepping from sunlight into shadow could mean a drop in temperature of a couple of hundred degrees. This is one reason why temperature-regulated space suits would be a necessity on the moon. Merely being encased in an airtight covering would not afford sufficient protection.

*

Light and Shade on the Moon

H. PERCY WILKINS

THE time is approaching when men will land amid the weird landscapes of the moon and, among other strange things, will experience a remarkable sequence of light and shade. It is known that any atmosphere must be of extreme tenuity; even from the earth we can see the blackness of the lunar shadows, an indication of the rarity of the atmosphere because there is no scattering and diffusion of light as occurs on the earth.

Yet, despite the deepness of the shadows, the distribution of light on the moon is, in some respects, greater than with ourselves. Much would depend upon the location of the observer, who we will suppose is on the side which faces the earth.

At night the stars must shine with a brilliancy unknown to ourselves, and the amount of starlight will be very appreciable. It is nearly lost in the light reflected from the earth which, as seen from the moon, would appear as a huge disk, 13 times as great in area and, when fully illuminated, giving 60 times as much light as the moon does to ourselves. For an observer situated in what is to us the center of the moon's disk, the earth would be overhead and as one traveled north or south or east or west, so would the earth appear to sink in the sky until it would touch the horizon. This would be the state of things for anybody situated at what is to us the edge or limb.

Although the earth would not remain exactly fixed in the lunar sky, its movements would be small and only noticeable for places where our planet was near the horizon. There is a zone in which the earth is sometimes visible and at other times invisible, what we know as the libratory regions, bordering the mysterious hidden side of the moon.

Imagine an observer placed at neither the center nor the edge of the moon, but at an intermediate point; let us select the crater Theophilus. For him, midnight would see the earth in a gibbous phase, like the moon three days before full and a little more than halfway up the sky. So intense must be the light reflected by the earth, that everything would be brightly illuminated so that the

H. Percy Wilkins, from *Journal of the British Interplanetary Society,* Vol. 15, No. 2, March-April, 1956.

mountains in the center of the crater and the crater walls would cast black shadows. The earth is "full" in the "early hours," always remembering that on the moon the night lasts fourteen times as long as with ourselves.

The actual amount of light reflected by the earth will vary because of its rotation on its axis and also on account of the variable amount of cloud in our atmosphere. Once in a little over twenty-four hours there must be a certain falling off in the reflected light, when most of the earth's disk is occupied by the vast expanse of the Pacific Ocean. On the other hand, when Asia, Africa, and Europe face the moon, these great land surfaces strongly reflect the sunlight into space.

As the night advances, the earth loses its roundness and a dark sickle begins to invade it on one side. Meanwhile, a bright cone of light has made its appearance in the east and this acts, to some extent, in opposition to the light of the earth. This cone is the zodiacal light which is much more intense as seen from the moon than from the earth. Eventually the streamers of the sun's corona mingle with the zodiacal light; the mountains cast dual shadows until suddenly, the first speck of the sun's disk appears above the dark horizon.

On the moon, the sun takes about an hour to rise and, for the first few minutes, the small portion visible gives a twilight effect. Also the shadows bear a considerable penumbral fringe owing to the fact that the sun is a disk and not a point of light. At the same time, a ray of direct sunshine is much more intense, by comparison, than the feeble light of the earth.

During the lunar morning, and again in the afternoon, the otherwise black shadows, with their penumbral fringes, are partially relieved by reflection from sunlit cliffs and, to a limited amount, by the light of the earth. The latter, however, rapidly diminishes as the sun rises higher above the horizon and approaches the almost stationary earth, now in crescent form.

There is a certain blue tint to the sunshine since there is no atmospheric mantle to absorb this part of the spectrum as happens on the earth. Strongly colored light is experienced only when the sun is eclipsed by the earth during what is to us an eclipse of the moon [Plate XVII]. Then the predominating hue is red, very intense for those places which are deeply immersed in the earth's shadow, but fading into a rose tint for other regions.

The lunar rocks will exhibit marked colors because there is no weather to obliterate them and their visibility is affected by the angle of illumination which is always changing on the moon.

At midday at Theophilus there are no shadows, the sun shines in full strength and so continues until passing the now invisible earth, when shadow begins to appear along the crater slopes. As the sun sinks in the sky, the shadows increase and the crescent earth reflects sufficient light to relieve their intense blackness. With the disappearance of the sun the cone of the zodiacal light adds its quota to the light of the earth, the light of which gets stronger and stronger as the night draws on.

This is the eternally repeated pattern of light and shade on the moon and the grand result is that the lunar landscape is always illuminated to a greater or a lesser extent. We can easily be misled by the telescopic view, when the apparently intense black shadows suggest a total darkness within them. The truth is that sometimes they are illuminated by many times the intensity of our moonlight; it is the adjacent, directly sunlit portions which make them seem intense.

For Theophilus, the night illumination is dimmest soon after sunset, when the earth is a crescent, and is greatest in the morning "early hours," when the earth is full, but for other portions of the moon the distribution is different and may be reversed. On the moon, the only really black places are the interiors of those craters, or the sides of those mountains, from which neither the sun nor the earth is ever visible. This condition applies to regions close to one of the poles, especially the south. The most pleasant landing spot for spaceships, from the consideration of the distribution of light, will be near the center of the disk, and the crater of Ptolemy [Plate XII] may well be the spot selected. There the earth is full at midnight, and being always near the zenith, its light is always reflected straight onto the surface so that total blackness is unknown both by day and by night.

* Mining on the Moon

The problems connected with a lunar base are of a peculiar kind that require contributions from a variety of experts, often in fields that ordinarily have little concern with bodies astronomical. Those who have ventured to make comments on the lunar base usually assume it to be already a going concern, with underground living quarters, a power supply, and some means of obtaining the necessities of existence, either on the spot or by import from the earth. Under these assumptions it is not too difficult to go a step farther and picture the development of the base from the natural resources available. The only criticism one would make of these projects is that their authors are perhaps overoptimistic about finding the minerals they require concentrated within a narrow radius on the moon. If such minerals are not readily available it is going to go hard with the struggling young colony, for certainly ore cannot be transported for any considerable distances in large quantities. Therefore, development of the lunar base is likely to be slow or end in disaster unless the first arrivals are extremely lucky in their choice of landing site. Assuming that something of the sort occurs, it is interesting to get the views of a mining engineer of the lines along which development of the base might proceed assuming reasonable luck in obtaining natural resources. It matters little if we disagree with some of the remarks made. What is important is starting people to think realistically along wholly new lines which until recently were considered the exclusive property of fantasy or science fiction.

*

Development of a Lunar Base

G. E. V. AWDRY

FEW mining engineers seem to have joined the British Interplanetary Society, perhaps understandably. A layman can be forgiven for considering some of the problems which will arise in the field of mining and metallurgy during the development of a lunar base, with a view to making this base as useful as possible, while keeping the cost in supplies brought in down to the minimum. The solutions advanced may or may not be valid, but these are real problems which call for attention.

It is assumed that a small permanent base has been established underground for scientific research, with the obvious laboratory and field equipment, and that plentiful electrical power is available, either from solar heat or nuclear energy. A regular, though infrequent, shuttle plies between the moon and an orbit about the earth, so that anything worth the energy cost can be imported. The base uses algae tanks to replace oxygen consumed, and to grow its food, any wastage being made up by imports. The moon itself is assumed to consist of complex silicates, similar to unweathered igneous rocks on earth, probably with much uncombined silica, and volatile or stable compounds having been dissipated.

I am not competent to discuss mining in detail. But for some time the ores will be a by-product of excavations for additional living and storage space. The expedition must have come prepared to do some tunneling, in order to get underground, so equipment will be available. The aim should be at first to use explosives as little as possible. Their transport will be an appreciable item. Meanwhile, a core drill will be a better choice, say one of 6 inches diameter. The cutting head should be tipped with tungsten carbide, or industrial diamonds, so that only these relatively light items need be imported as consumed. Silicates are hard and abrasive, but mostly brittle, and wedges, thermal shock, or even hammers will probably serve to break down the working face once enough holes have been drilled. Later on, liquid oxygen will become available for blasting, and boring may be done with an iron pipe, burning in oxygen fed through it. This method is already in use, and will melt concrete. It should be

G. E. V. Awdry, from *Journal of the British Interplanetary Society*, Vol. 13, No. 3, May, 1954.

particularly useful in association with thermal shock produced by injecting a little liquid oxygen afterward. Tunneling under these conditions will be heavy work, and should be carried out in an atmosphere, if the rock is firm, to avoid physical distress. Dust respirators, however, will be essential, to prevent silicosis. None of this excavation will be wasted, as prudence will demand that the base be subdivided into sections connected by tunnels with emergency air locks.

The simplest means of transport will be by suspended railway, at first with manual haulage, later electrified. This uses one rail instead of two, and fewer wheels as well—a considerable saving in metal at installation—though wear will be higher. It can be easily suspended from the roof, by something resembling the familiar Rawlplug. It will have a further advantage as the base becomes extensive and speeds rise, for such a system is naturally stable under centrifugal force on curves. The conventional railway depends on gravity, assisted by superelevation of the outer rail, to resist this force, and lunar gravity is dangerously weak for the purpose, unless an impracticably broad gauge is adopted. In the reduced gravity, gradients need not be so carefully avoided, but some means will have to be found to increase adhesion at starts. Electrical drive applied to all wheels might suffice, or spring-loaded rollers underneath the rail which could be engaged or disengaged at need. Brakes should be of the electromagnetic sledge type commonly used on tramways.

Silicates are unpromising ores by their abrasiveness, the large quantities needed for a given yield of metal, the close association of several metals in any one sample, and the great bulk of tailings. These latter present a less immediate problem on the moon, being silica, which can be used as an insulator, or fused and formed into many useful articles, notably tanks and piping for ore processing. It will be worth-while to subject the tailings to heat treatment in any case, to recover the last traces of reagents and water. The first ore treated will be lunar dust, which will need no grinding. Later on, it will be possible to build an old-fashioned tube mill, in which the larger lumps of ore will do the actual grinding, thus saving the need for hard-wearing steels at some cost in efficiency and time. But power is plentiful. The dust is leached with acids, and the liquor subjected to a series of selective precipitations, until it contains only sodium and potassium salts, when it can be concentrated and electrolyzed to yield these metals or their hydroxides, which will be needed to leach out aluminum. Heat treatment, or electrolysis, will recover water or acids still locked up in the precipitates.

The various metals will call for different methods of treatment. Pure iron can be deposited electrolytically from a sulphate solution, if the bath is topped up with iron oxide from time to time. Calcium, which may be useful as a bearing metal under airless conditions, can be electrolyzed out of fused oxide, magnesium from its chloride. Even aluminum can be plated out of a nonaqueous solution with an admixture of lithium hydride. Wherever possible, to save reprocessing, metals should be deposited in molds, so that the article needs only finishing. Where powder metallurgy can be used, this also makes a worthwhile saving in time and plant.

More conventional reduction processes call for greater thought. If enough alkali metal is readily available, aluminum can be reduced with this instead of carbon, while a simple cyclic process can be used to reduce iron. Hydrogen passed over heated iron oxide is partly oxidized, reducing the oxide to iron. Water vapor is extracted from the gas by metallic sodium, which reaction replaces half the hydrogen. The rest is recovered by electrolyzing the sodium hydroxide formed, and the water evolved in this electrolysis.

It will be easier, however, if we can avoid using so elusive and bulky a gas as hydrogen as a reducing agent. The alternative is carbon, or its monoxide. By hypothesis, we have on the moon no source of carbon such as coal, but we have in the algae tanks the means of fixing it from its dioxide, and the algae can be distilled to yield a reasonably pure carbon. Briquetted with the pitch that will be another product of this distillation and baked, this will provide usable electrodes for an arc furnace. It will be necessary, in any case, to have extra tank capacity available, in case of breakdown at the base or sudden arrival of additional inhabitants, and it may as well be in constant operation. Possibly, the algae could be left in the dark, or otherwise kept dormant, but this is a waste of capacity when they can be put to good use. To maintain the cycle, the other distillation products must be oxidized and recycled, but that should be straightforward enough. On the basis of a recent paper, 1 liter of solution containing 55 gm. algae produces a usable surplus of 2.5 gm. algae daily. It is reasonable to suppose that 20 per cent of this yield is readily recoverable as usable carbon, so that 2 cv. m. of liquid will yield daily 1 kg. electrodes, enough to reduce, in theory, 3 kg. aluminum or 7 kg. iron (from a mixture of both oxides, quoted as a mean figure).

There are still considerable difficulties. In order to reduce worth-while quantities of metal, very large tanks will be needed to recycle the carbon. Mining operations will soon provide space for these. Fluorine, or its compounds, are always found in the gases resulting from aluminum reduction, due to the breakdown of the cryolite used as flux. It should not be difficult to separate these off by inducing them to combine with some base or metal relatively inert to carbon dioxide. In case carbon monoxide is present, oxygen ought to be added to these gases while hot, and this may present technical difficulties. There will be an inevitable wastage of reagents used for leaching, and of carbon and water. Perhaps the ores themselves will yield enough of the latter, included as water of crystallization, but the others will have to be replaced. Sulphur may be present. If not, it can be imported, and converted to acid on the moon. There will be no point in hauling up oxygen. Nitrogen, combined as hydrazine, is a likely rocket fuel, and prudence will indicate building up stocks, from which a little can be spared for conversion to nitric acid. If the chosen oxidant is nitric acid, it will be well worth-while making this on the moon from hydrazine, at least for the return trip. Fluorine is a constituent of some igneous rocks, but will otherwise have to be imported. Carbon is the most important item, for there will be consumption as well as loss, steel containing up to 1.5 per cent. But a little ingenuity can be used here. Activated carbon is an excellent insulator for liquid oxygen tanks, but gelatinous silica—which leaching operations will produce in enormous quantities—is an acceptable substitute, and could replace it for the earthward trip.

Whatever else is scarce on the moon, oxygen will be abundant. A ton will be extracted in the reduction of 2.625 tons of iron, or 1.125 tons of aluminum, 1,000 days' supply for a man, with no recycling. There will be leakage losses, but on nothing like this scale. The moon will be able, therefore, to supply all space craft and artificial satellites except those departing from earth. It seems essential, also, despite the long transit time, to adopt ion-drive, at least for freight shuttles, between the earth satellite and circumlunar orbit. Spitzer has shown that an acceptable performance can be achieved by a vehicle using nitrogen accelerated to 100 km/sec as reaction mass. Allowing for differences in atomic weight, the same installations would presumably accelerate oxygen to about 80 km/sec. This apparently gives a mass ratio for oxygen equal to the 5/4 power of the "nitrogen" mass ratio, which would be tolerable for a relatively short haul, and oxygen need not be brought up from earth, as nitrogen would have to be. The ionizing grids might present some difficulty owing to the danger of corrosion. But one cannot imagine the United States promoting an export from the moon which will only entail further excavations at Fort Knox, so that gold, if it is found, will be merely another metal, to be put to any use for which it is suited. Being very ductile, and a good conductor of heat and electricity, as well as being immune to oxidation, it should be an excellent material for ionizing grids, if it can be adequately supported.

From this it appears that the necessities of life and development can be made available without excessive cost, and that the hope of using the resources of the moon to open the solar system to exploration is a good one. The main obstacle will be time, for until enough development has been done to support a larger population, any progress can only be gradual. But much can be done without massive equipment, and with the import only of essentials. Very few of these need be consumable stores.

* Power on the Moon

Assuming we are able to place men on the moon sometime, the problem is
what to do with them after arrival. Shall the men be wholly dependent on
their supply line with the earth? Or will they attempt to become self-sufficient
on the moon? The latter course is much to be preferred if it is humanly possible. Here we are handicapped by our exceedingly scanty knowledge of what
materials compose the lunar surface. We have to proceed pretty much by guess-
work from the slender information available to us. The lunar station has been
discussed many times, the power problem usually being casually dismissed with
the remark that power can be obtained in ample quantities from the sun. But
it might not be so easy. Here is probably one of the most realistic and detailed
discussions of this important problem that so far has appeared in print. It is
taken from the Lunar and Planetary Colloquium held in Los Angeles, consisting of a group of scientists and technicians who meet for rather informal discussion of the scientific aspects of planetary exploration. The speaker's often
extemporaneous remarks are recorded, and then have to be put in a form suitable for publication. This accounts for some of the peculiarities in style found
in these papers.

Aside from the purely scientific aspect of the problems opened up for exploration here, one of the most interesting points raised is the answer to the
oft repeated question, "Why go to the moon?" Dr. O'Day of the Cambridge
Research Center, ARDC, attempts to give no practical reasons for such a project. His answer is simply that man will colonize the moon because that is part
of his destiny.

*

Power for a Lunar Colony

MARCUS O'DAY

THE problem of utilization of solar energy on the moon is simple compared to that on the earth, but how you are going to use this solar energy on the moon depends a good deal on what you want to do with it. So I want to discuss a number of things that you could do with solar energy.

But before I do that, I'd like to emphasize that I am assuming the most hostile environment that you can have, namely, that what you will be dealing with mostly will be of the composition of the igneous rocks, that approximately half of the moon's surface will be of silicon dioxide, and that we will also find aluminum oxide, magnesium oxide, sodium oxide, and so forth. This means a chemistry without water. And that is very serious. I do think that the chemist has to get himself into a little different state of mind due to the fact that he has to think of nonaqueous chemistry. One of the things which I feel will be an absolute necessity on the moon is a liquid, and in looking at the various things that we might find, I had assumed that sodium chloride would be on the moon. I don't know how good that assumption is, but it's a fairly common material. We could break it down electrolytically, and use the chlorine with silicon, to get silicon tetrachloride. This material would be very important if we have an engine on the moon.

Some astronomers believe that they have discovered deposits of sulfur on the moon. If so, this discovery makes possible the use of another liquid in a heat engine; namely, sulfur dioxide. This liquid would be obtained by burning sulfur with the oxygen which has resulted from the electrolysis of one of the fused salts. The probability that this liquid will be available is apparently much greater than the probability that chlorine will be discovered on the moon.

Now, there are four types of devices which have been proposed for capturing solar power: the lens, the parabolic reflector, the flat plate collector, and the solar battery. I would like to discuss these four things as they would be on the moon. Now before I start, let us think of the properties of the moon that are different from what we are used to. The first has to do with the period of rota-

Marcus O'Day, from *Proceedings of the Lunar and Planetary Exploration Colloquium,* October 29, 1958.

tion of the moon which is only once in about twenty-eight days instead of once every twenty-four hours as with the earth. This fact is extremely important. It's important from the standpoint of how we will use solar energy; and it's extremely important from the standpoint of any electrochemistry which we will have on the moon as a result of our solar power. Next we will assume that there is almost a perfect vacuum on the moon. We have to think a lot about this feature because it's not just a question of living in an enclosed atmosphere; it involves a great many of the things which we may want to do. At first when you think about living on the moon, you think it's an extremely hostile environment, and after continuing to think about it for a while, you get, shall we say, accustomed to the idea, and you realize there are certain advantages there. For one thing, you don't have any weather; everything is perfectly predictable; you have no wind, and as a consequence you have no dust problem.

The fact that there is no wind enormously simplifies the problem of having a large lens or a large reflector. The Russians have probably done more on the utilization of solar energy than any other people, and I've read a number of the Russian articles. Most of the articles are concerned with the structure which holds the reflector, and with the fact that on earth this structure with its wind-loading is enormously expensive. But if you have no wind to worry about, and no dust to foul the surface of your reflector or your lens, that problem is comparatively simple. You could have very, very lightweight reflectors. For some of the things which I had in mind you might be able to have a light plastic Fresnel type of lens, a very large lens. The reason I would like a lens is that I want to melt the silicon dioxide. Silicon dioxide melts at about 1,700° C., and you have the same trouble there as the thermonuclear people have. They say, "What's going to contain this hot plasma?" Well, they have a magnetic bottle. We can't use that on the moon, so we'll have to use the materials existing there. We'll have to focus the rays of the sun on the lunar surface and melt it. A lens is very much better for that than a mirror because a mirror requires at least one auxiliary reflector. So, if we are going to think of an electrochemistry up there with very high temperatures—and we can get these high temperatures with a large lens, or with a series of large reflectors—we will be able to melt whatever we're considering.

I have more or less concentrated on silicon dioxide in my thinking. Now we haven't used silicon very much. I know only about three uses for it. One of them is in connection with transformer iron; we have the silicon solar battery; and it can be used for transistors and thermocouples. At first, I had the idea that one would just electrolize this silicon dioxide, but the first chemist I talked to told me that we can't separate silicon dioxide by an electric current. The group of chemists at the center where I am now have suggested that perhaps the best thing to do would be to use magnesium silicate, which can be electrolized. Scientifically, I suppose there's no real problem there, and we'll have the direct current, as I'll indicate in a few moments. But we do have some technological problems, and the big technological problem is that our carbon electrode will probably be consumed by the oxygen which is liberated. And, of course, if you have to transport the carbon electrode from the earth, that is going to be a major problem. I'm certainly hoping that we will find some form of carbon up there that we can use on a permanent basis.

By the way, I am giving this talk on the assumption that there has been an initial exploratory expedition to the moon, that you have some people there, that they have an atomic or nuclear device for the production of power, in short, that they've been able to do some preliminary things. What I'm talking about is the next step, where perhaps you have a hundred people you want to put there, and then this colony of a hundred people will grow, and be self-sufficient. The lack of carbon, water, and nitrogen is extremely serious. Undoubtedly we may find these things, but we may not, and they will have to be brought from the earth and be conserved very tightly.

As I thought about this problem, I couldn't see these people living in plastic bubbles which are extremely vulnerable to meteoric impact; and also I don't think people could live very well without protection against the cosmic rays which come from the sun. So I have thought of having a pretty substantial structure with the roof perhaps 10 or 12 feet thick, so they would be able to live in comparative safety.

Going back to the production of electricity, I would use a parabolic reflector for focusing the rays of the sun on thermocouples. And I've thought of the houses as being made up of very large thermocouples on the side. Now it was mentioned this morning that we expect to have iron there. What could be the other element of the thermocouple? Well, silicon is something which I think could be used very well. Silicon doped with about 6 per cent aluminum which is on the moon as an oxide should give an electrical conductivity which is suitable. I had figured on the sides of the house being, say, columns of doped silicon about 30 feet high, and about one meter in cross section. Right next to each of those would be a column of iron which would be one centimeter in thickness and one meter wide. Assuming that you had a temperature of 1,000 or more degrees, you'd get about one kilowatt from each pair of thermocouples. This would give a good direct current for our electrochemistry. Now we will want electrical power for other things, but with a reasonable structure we could get somewhere around 50 volts from thermocouples of this type.

Of course, we are going to have many very lightweight reflectors focusing the rays of the sun. But these, I assume, can be obtained comparatively easily. After you have been there for some time and have made your silicon cells, I have assumed that you would then make these reflectors out of the silicon cells, because the silicon cells reflect approximately 50 per cent of the light that strikes upon them. Thus you would have electrical power from both the thermocouples and the silicon cells. One reason why I have been so strong for the thermocouple is that I feel we must store heat for the long nights; you have two weeks of night as well as two weeks of sunshine. The fact that there is a vacuum makes the insulation against heat transfer extremely easy. There are only two methods of transferring heat on the moon. One is by radiation and the other is by conduction. It is comparatively easy to insulate against both. In the case of radiation, for instance, all you have to do is to install a reflector to prevent radiation into space.

This ease of insulation has a tremendous effect on our thinking about how we will use solar energy on the moon. Take the matter of the storage of our heat, for instance. I have assumed that perhaps we should store heat by melted silicon dioxide and use this latent heat of fusion for growing the food and so forth, during the long lunar night. You do not want to stop your process of photosynthesis, so after the sun goes down you will still require light to keep plants growing.

Now I did some calculation on how much silicon dioxide we would have to have melted if we didn't want to let the temperature drop below 1,710° C. to the point where the silicon dioxide would solidify. Well, some of these figures are astounding. Three thousand large calories, or kilocalories, per person per day is what you must have in the food, and assuming one half of 1 per cent for the photosynthetic efficiency, it turns out that you would need about 27 cubic meters of material per person, a cube 3 meters on a side. That's very large, and after you start thinking about it, you begin to realize how fortunate we are here on the earth. We have all the energy that has been stored chemically by the sun and the vegetation, and so forth, not to mention the energy that was stored in geologic times. But this is just one of the facts of life. If we're going to store energy during the dark period, and if we're going to store it by the latent heat of fusion of silicon dioxide, which is about 135 calories per gram, then we will require that amount of material; and we will have to melt it and insulate it against loss of heat. We hope that there are more efficient ways of growing food than have been indicated in the study so far. One half of 1 per cent is pretty low, but I understand that if you increase the carbon dioxide content, making it about 5 per cent, and have the proper temperature, you might run up the photosynthetic efficiency to about 5 per cent. That's one of our problems, and we must keep it very much in mind.

Now the use of the flat plate, which is considered a great deal for solar energy on the earth, is comparatively simple on the moon. The reason is because we have a vacuum. And if we take something like silicon tetrachloride as a working substance, and want to heat it beneath a flat plate, we will simply coat that plate with a material that absorbs in the visible, and reflects in the infrared. A number of materials were suggested at the Solar Energy Conference several years ago. I happen to know that tungsten has such a surface very similar to that. I am told that if you put a tungsten lamp out in the sunlight, and look at it laterally, you will find that the filament is at a much higher temperature than red hot. That is, there are materials that are absorptive in the visible region and reflective in the infrared. The Israelis are doing a great deal of work on such materials.

So, if we use a flat plate with one of these materials on the top, and have some type of rough louver to prevent radiation into the other part of the sky, we should be able to get a temperature of several hundred degrees. A piece of absorptive material exposed to direct sunlight will reach a temperature of about 112° C., a temperature that is comparable to the temperature of the subsolar point on the moon. If we have this material at such a high temperature and circulate our working fluid, it can be taken to an engine; and the engine can drive a generator to give power at a voltage which is suitable for a machine shop. Of course, I might mention the technical problem of lubrication in a vacuum under those conditions, but I'm fortunate in being a physicist and not having to worry about engineering problems, so I'll just throw them out to you.

A solar battery would give power at a voltage somewhere between what you might get from your generator with a heat engine from the thermocouple. As I said before, the thermocouple would give us power at about the right voltage for an electrochemical industry. And I would assume we would have a very large electrochemical industry after many people are there. You would just have to have it in order to provide for their needs. And I've based it a good deal, as I've said, on silicon. I believe very strongly that we ought to start work now on the development of a silicon technology. One of the things that irritated me when I tried to get out data on silicon for preparing this paper was that one group of people will be interested, say, in transistors and they'll dope silicon for that purpose, but they'll never measure the other properties. Another group of people are interested in electrical resistivity, and they'll measure that, but never get anything else. For the development of a silicon technology (and I believe that silicon can be an extremely useful material) one needs to know *all* the properties. Every group of people who are doing anything with silicon should be set up, as a matter of routine, to measure all the normal properties, the mechanical properties, the electrical resistivity, the thermal conductivity, the thermoelectric power, and other things like the Hall effect. That would enable other people to run some suitable calculations. I think that unless you have all the properties tabulated, then you have wasted a tremendous amount of research money. So I'm pleading right now for the development of a silicon technology in which all of these properties are determined, so that theoretical people can use them.

I talked a moment ago about storing up power for the lunar night for the growing of food. There is one thing that will help us in obtaining light for the photosynthetic process, viz., earthshine. There is approximately 75 times as much light that the man on the moon will get from the earth as we get from the full moon. The moon always keeps the same surface toward the earth, so that a person on the moon watching the earth doesn't see it rise and set. Now if he uses the same reflectors to focus the light from the earth, then this will help considerably in getting the energy for the photosynthetic process. (I mention that because in these considerations we have to think of all the little things which affect our work.)

If the colony is on the meridian facing the earth it will never see during the lunar night less than half the earth, so that the amount of earthshine will only vary between these limits one half to the full amount.

I've covered the matter of getting silicon and oxygen; I understand people can breathe pure oxygen at reduced pressure, but it's hard on the lungs. So we should manufacture some inert gas that will dilute the oxygen. If we don't find carbon there, we shall have to take it there.

I have thought of the problem of water. As you know, the earth is bombarded, and of course the moon too, by protons from the sun. I took the figures that have been published on the aurora and the density of protons, and calculated that over the two or three billion years during which the moon has been exposed to the sun—of course one face would be exposed for only half that time, as the other side was away from the sun—about 10^{22} atoms of hydrogen would have struck the moon's surface. Those are cosmic rays; they would have penetrated down for quite a distance, and I think we can assume that in the energy interchange those atoms would have been trapped. So, we may find a source of hydrogen, and it has probably combined with oxygen to form water, perhaps 10 feet below the surface of the moon. It wouldn't be very much, but when you haven't any, a little is a lot.

As I have thought about it more and more, I have been more and more convinced that it may not, at the time when a colony is formed, be more difficult to put a self-sufficient colony on the moon than it was to put a colony on the North American continent. People have asked me, "Why colonize the moon? That seems to be a crazy idea," and, of course, in many ways it is. But my answer to that is a sort of religious one. You remember that the Psalmist, speaking of man, said, "Thou hast created him only a little lower than God, and hast crowned him with glory and honor." I would say that man will colonize the moon, not for military reasons, but because there is a little bit of God in man, and it drives him on, and on, and on. He'll colonize the moon because that's part of his destiny.

* Lunar Agriculture

At first it sounds fantastic. Growing vegetables on the moon. Yet if we succeed in establishing a lunar base there is no reason why it cannot be done. In fact, it *must* be done, otherwise we never can say that we have accomplished the conquest of space. Besides manufacturing oxygen and water the colony must also be able to provide its own food supply from vegetables grown on the moon itself.

Obviously farming cannot be carried out on the open surface of the moon. Plants have to be surrounded by an atmosphere from which they can take carbon dioxide and oxygen. They must have water which cannot be supplied to them in the usual way by sprinkling or irrigation ditches, as the water would evaporate immediately in a vacuum. Furthermore, the surface of the moon is utterly sterile. It has no topsoil to supply plants with the ingredients needed for proper growth.

It would be necessary therefore that farming be carried out in airtight enclosures, where conditions suitable for plant growth can be provided artificially and maintained under complete control. This naturally will be a considerable undertaking, but if we are capable of sending manned vehicles to the moon in the first place, we certainly should possess the technical know-how to care for the crews later. Fortunately, hydroponic farming has already been thoroughly tested on the earth, so that introducing it on the moon will not be a new experiment. Moreover, it is something that can be tried on the earth beforehand under accurately simulated lunar conditions. What a thrill it will be—eating the first vegetables grown on the moon!

*

Farming on the Moon

J. W. E. H. SHOLTO DOUGLAS

ONE of the first problems to confront a potential lunar colony is the provision of an adequate supply of food. Without assurance of sufficient nutriment to sustain at least minimum standards of health and vigor, exploration of unknown territories is impossible. The pages of history are in fact filled with pitiful and calamitous accounts of the fate that has so frequently overtaken brave and intrepid voyagers who, after the exhaustion of their resources and stores, have at length succumbed to the pangs of hunger.

Many of these disasters could, however, have been avoided had the expeditions in question possessed the technical equipment for food production that we have today. It is now practicable for scientists on earth to cultivate vegetable and cereal crops in practically any area on earth, independently of the soil or local conditions, in a very short space of time.

Hydroponics. During the past two decades, very successful results in plant growing have been achieved by means of soilless cultivation in areas where ordinary methods of farming are inpracticable. This system of crop production is generally known as hydroponics, a word derived from Greek and translatable as "water-working." By using hydroponics, plants may be raised in the absence of organic matter by feeding them on solutions of chemicals containing all the elements essential to healthy development and fruiting. Apart from enabling crops to be grown in places where conventional farming is impossible, soilless culture also gives very much larger yields, combined with quicker growth and lower space requirements, since the provision of adequate nutriment is guaranteed and the method provides complete control over the plants. These important advantages would become factors of considerable significance under lunar conditions.

The Green Plant. In order to appreciate fully the problems to be faced in es-

J. W. E. H. Sholto Douglas, "Farming on the Moon, The Possibility of Utilizing Soilless Cultures to Produce Crops under Lunar Conditions," from *Journal of the British Interplanetary Society,* Vol. 15, No. 1, January-February, 1956.

tablishing farms and gardens on the moon, it is useful to recall briefly the essentials of plant growth, at least as we know them on earth. The study of plant nutrition is a vast and complex subject, and it is not possible here to give more than an outline of certain salient points and the fundamentals of crop physiology. Growth is the natural result of certain chemical changes which take place regularly in all vital organisms. This gradual building up of living matter requires suitable surroundings and adequate nutrition and, in the case of the green plant, these essentials consist of water, air, light, mineral salts, and a support for the root.

As green plants, unlike animals, cannot ingest solid or organic food material owing to the presence of the cell wall, they are obliged to absorb part of their nourishment from the air, and part from solutions of inorganic salts or chemicals. These simple substances are built up by the various departments of the plants into living protoplasm through the expenditure of energy. How this energy is obtained is a subject of fascinating interest, for while the bulk of an animal's food, consisting as it does of fats, proteins, and carbohydrates, contains a large store of potential energy, the simple inorganic diet of a plant is virtually devoid of any such efficiency. The answer is, of course, that plants possess the ability to build up sugars and other carbohydrates from compounds such as water and carbon dioxide, using light as the source of energy. This process is known as carbon assimilation or photosynthesis, and can only be carried on when light acts upon chlorophyll in the presence of water. Chlorophyll, which is the green coloring matter in plants, enables the sun's radiant energy to bring about such an amazing transformation. A special relationship exists between plants and animals, called the carbon cycle. A plant absorbs carbon dioxide from the air through stomata situated on the underside of the leaves, while, as a by-product of photosynthesis, oxygen is liberated. Animals on the other hand, breathe in oxygen and exhale carbon dioxide. Plants do, however, need some oxygen since it forms the basis of important processes which form a part of normal growth. In addition to air, light, and water, certain mineral salts are required for the production of chlorophyll, and the other functions preceding and following photosynthesis. These elements in conjunction with water are absorbed by the root hairs, utilizing the force of osmosis, while the roots themselves are supported in nature by the firmness of the soil in which they rest.

Essentials of Growth. The first of the five essentials for healthy plant growth to be considered in greater detail is water. Chemically, pure water is a compound consisting of two parts hydrogen to one part oxygen, but in actual practice, it often contains traces of other elements. In many fruits, water constitutes 90 per cent of the total weight, in green foliage leaves it is often as high as 80 per cent, while even in "dry" seeds 10 to 12 per cent may frequently be found. In fact, germination cannot take place in the absence of sufficient moisture. Another phenomenon for which plants need ample water is transpiration, e.g., the cells in a leaf give up water in the form of vapor to the atmosphere when exposed to dry air. Unless this water is replaced, the cells will lose their turgidity and the leaf wilts. Of the elements necessary to plant life, all but carbon and to a lesser extent oxygen are derived from the water containing dissolved mineral substances or chemicals which is being continually absorbed by the roots. Even an appreciable amount of oxygen is obtained from this source. Osmosis, already mentioned, is vital to plant life, since it is by this means that water containing chemical nutrients is taken in by the root hairs and circulated through the plant, where its presence is essential for the complicated and intricate process of carbon assimilation or photosynthesis.

Sunshine consists of many different kinds of light rays, but experiments have shown that the green leaf synthesizes carbohydrates most actively in blue and red light. The importance of illumination is that it supplies the energy necessary for the conversion of carbon dioxide into organic compounds, while chlorophyll provides the mechanism by means of which this light energy is made available for the process. The rate of photosynthesis is affected by such factors as the intensity of illumination and the supply of carbon dioxide. Poor light results in little activity, while brilliant sunshine generally means rapid reaction.

Green plants derive the greater part of their food requirement from the air, and over 40 per cent of their dry matter is accounted for by carbon obtained from the carbon dioxide in the atmosphere. This gas, together with oxygen, diffuses through the stomata into the foliage, where it is built up, as we already know, into sugars and other carbohydrates for the nourishment of the growing plant. An important process for which air is essential is respiration, or the taking in of oxygen. Here again the gas enters the plant through the stomata, diffuses throughout the spaces between each cell and finally passes into solution. Together with the oxygen derived from the water absorbed by the roots, it meets the plants' requirements of this element. Respiration itself is an interesting function, being the exact reverse of photosynthesis.

The following equations may be used to express these processes:

$$\textit{Photosynthesis} \quad 6CO_2 + 6H_2O \quad \rightarrow \quad C_6H_{12}O_6 + 6O_2$$
$$\textit{Respiration} \quad C_6H_{12}O_6 + 6O_2 \quad \rightarrow \quad 6H_2O + 6CO_2$$

It will of course be appreciated that neither process is quite so simple as these equations represent.

Chemical analysis of plant material has revealed that about forty different mineral elements are concerned with the processes of growth and nutrition, but out of these only fourteen are of vital concern. The absorption of carbon, hydrogen, and oxygen has already been discussed, and the point made that all the other elements found present have been taken up in solution by the roots. These chemicals may be divided into two classes, namely the major elements and the trace elements. The former are required in relatively abundant proportions, while the latter are needed in very minute quantities only.

Nitrogen is extremely important for the production of proteins in plants. It promotes leaf and stem growth, makes for good foliage, and healthy appearance, being in fact the foundation upon which the life substance, or protoplasm, is built up.

Phosphorus stimulates the production of flowers and fruits, encourages healthy root growth, expedites the process of ripening, and generally results in improved quality.

Potassium plays a vital part in the synthesis of sugars and starch within the plant. It hardens and strengthens the tissues and framework while generally improving fructification.

Calcium seems to stimulate root growth and to strengthen the cell walls.

Magnesium enters into chlorophyll formation, and it may act as a transporting agent for phosphorus.

Sulphur is an important plant food; it is associated with phosphorus, and is believed to assist the production of proteins.

Iron is essential for chlorophyll formation, and plays an important role in biological processes.

Manganese has certain rather complicated functions connected with nitrogen assimilation and reproduction. It is also said to improve the keeping quality of fruits and vegetables.

Boron has been known to stimulate the cell to abnormal growth and division.

Zinc is one of the elements essential to plant growth, but its exact role is still undefined.

Copper is believed to take part in chlorophyll formation.

In addition to these elements, several others can be mentioned briefly as a matter of interest. *Silicon* is considered to strengthen plant tissues; *chlorine* has been found to increase the water content of crops; *sodium* can perform certain of the functions of potassium and sometimes acts as an antidote against toxic salts; while *iodine,* as is well known, prevents the disease of goiter in human beings if present in the vegetables eaten by them.

The last essential for healthy growth is a suitable support for the roots. To stress such an obvious requirement may, at first glance, seem unnecessary, but unless the two-fold function of the roots can be satisfactorily executed, proper development will be impossible. Under natural conditions, plants derive both food and support from the earth, but as hydroponicists have pointed out, soil is in no way a perfect medium. Erosion, drought, and flood are big drawbacks, while it also harbors weeds, pests, and germs. Roots require a firm support, plenty of moisture without excess saturation, and plenty of aeration. Roots need to breathe just as much as leaves do. It is particularly important that their crowns should get plenty of oxygen from the air. For these reasons any good support for the roots, whether in soil or in soilless culture, is not only porous but capable of retaining moisture for a reasonable period. It also provides a firm basis for the growth and development of the plant from the young seedling stage right up to maturity.

Fungi and Algae. Before leaving the topic of plant nutrition, it is important to mention a few facts about one or two other classes of plants, which differ slightly from the green plant in mode of life. Some plants have no chlorophyll, for example the *fungi* (molds and toadstools), which includes the common mushroom. Such crops are incapable of synthesizing organic substances from simple inorganic compounds. They may obtain their food materials either from living organisms or from dead organic substances. In the former case, they are parasites, obtaining nutriment from the living cells of the host, but when they sustain themselves on dead organic matter, they are termed saprophytes. The saprophytes decompose organic bodies, breaking them down into simple compounds. The fungi differ fundamentally from normal green plants in their mode of nutrition. Since they do not possess any chlorophyll they are unable to synthesize carbohydrates from CO_2 and water. They derive their organic food material from complex carbon compounds which they obtain from external sources, and are able to absorb only soluble compounds. The hyphae secrete enzymes which convert insoluble substances to soluble ones, which are then absorbed. Although fungi are unable to make effective use of carbon dioxide, they can synthesize from soluble sugars the more complex carbohydrates which go to form their cell walls. Similarly, if supplied with carbohydrates and relatively simple nitrogenous compounds such as ammonium salts, they are able to synthesize proteins and eventually protoplasm. Ammonium salts do not, however, represent the only possible source of nitrogen. Many complex but soluble organic nitrogenous compounds can also be absorbed and utilized.

In addition to the fungi, a word or two about the *algae* would be appropriate. The algae are a multifarious group, but the unicellular varieties are most likely to be of interest to food producers. Trials have been undertaken in several areas to investigate the possibilities of growing algae for food. In contrast to higher green plants, these micro-organisms are unicellular, and being supported in water, have no skeleton other than the cell wall. Consequently, a greater proportion of their material may be devoted to useful purposes. Fifty per cent of the dry weight as protein is common, and up to 70 per cent has been obtained. In algae cultivation, all nutrients are applied in solution, there is no waste, and complete control can be secured over the crop. Algae need regular supplies of nutrient salts, ample light, and continuous agitation of the culture solution. A good level of carbon dioxide increases growth and yield. The most commonly grown organism has been *Chlorella*. The algae "farm" usually consists of tanks or tubes filled with water, to which nutrient salts are periodically added. The harvest is collected daily. As a human food, algae has good fat and vitamin content, but palatability depends upon preparation of the raw material.

Comparison of Terrestrial and Lunar Conditions. Naturally, in undertaking any transplantation of terrestrial vegetation to another planet, it would be necessary, in the initial stages at any rate, to supply the crops in question with the same fundamental requirements, but the possibility would exist of ultimately changing the new environment, and therefore in the end producing plants capable of withstanding vastly different conditions of life. By selection and breeding over a period of several years the cultivator would be able eventually to evolve crops capable of growing in quite extraordinary circumstances, unlike earth conditions—but of course that is a long-term project. At the start of any scheme of extraterrestrial colonization, crop production would necessarily be confined to creating environments similar to what plants have been accustomed to in this world.

In comparing conditions on the moon with those obtained on earth, as far as they are related to possible crop cultivation, the following items are of the greatest significance. In the first place, it may be assumed that there is no water in liquid form existing under lunar surface conditions, although there may well be frozen ice in some quantity in crevices, or underground. Secondly, the atmosphere is virtually negligible at lower levels, thus ruling out a supply of oxygen, or of carbon dioxide, in the free state, but there might be good possibilities of securing substantial amounts of these gases by release from the rocks on the moon. Light would of course be present, and the clear skies with absence of cloud (excepting any possible ground mist) would insure optimum sunshine. Here the question of temperature may be briefly touched on. During the lunar day, equivalent to fourteen of our earth days, the average noon temperatures on the surface of the crust are estimated to be 216° F., and during the long night the heat essential for plant growth would be entirely absent, since the temperature then falls to −243° F. Furthermore, terrestrial vegetation is accustomed to short periods of illumination, followed by a dark phase—the earth night—and would have to adapt itself to the different lunar conditions.

Finally, there are the other essentials of mineral salts, and a support for the roots, to consider. It is quite probable that chemical fertilizers could be produced on the moon, for feeding to crops, since no doubt the crust of that satellite is formed of much the same basic materials as is this globe, and all essential elements should be present, free or combined. There would be no soil, as we know it, and therefore no humus, making normal agriculture impossible. For hydroponic culture, however, there would be ample supplies of rock, which could be crushed into aggregate.

Problems To Be Faced. It will be at once obvious that the problems of agricultural development on the moon are formidable, but by no means insoluble. In the absence of air, water, and suitable temperatures, certain measures would have to be taken to create these essentials. Light would be quite satisfactory, but the different length of the days and nights would call for some adjustments. One or two other factors will also repay study, notably the low gravity—less than one sixth of the earth's—and the production of nutrients.

For various technical reasons, in particular the total absence of humus, and of soil bacteria, it would be impracticable to attempt to develop normal agriculture or gardening on the moon, even under the artificial domes of the colonies. Furthermore, it is most unlikely that sufficient space would ever be available for growth in soil to be attempted. Indeed, the only possible system for lunar conditions would be hydroponics, both for the above reasons and for the obtainment of the advantages mentioned earlier. The amount of data that has been accumulated up to date has made it possible for tentative plans to be drawn up for the eventual establishment of hydroponicums on the moon, large and efficient enough to provide ample supplies of all the vegetable foodstuffs for the use of the colonists living there. Naturally, many of the conclusions reached here are still based on hypothetical assumptions, and the preparation of final details must await the factual report of the first survey ship to reach our satellite. But it is surely time that an effort was made to stimulate thought on this subject, and that practical discussion should commence on what is, after all, a very vital matter.

Owing to the quite dissimilar atmospheres of the moon and the earth, the establishment of farms growing terrestrial crops for consumption by human beings living under lunar conditions would not be possible in the open. All of our plants need air, or water, or both, and there is no evidence to lead us to suppose that the moon is capable of retaining these in the free state at ground level. Consequently, some form of artificial contraption would be necessary to afford satisfactory protection to crops, and to conserve the supplies of water and air that would be provided for the plants. The most convenient structure would, no doubt be large domes or tubes, made of transparent material, so as to admit light. Inside such devices, the grower could create an environment giving optimum conditions for the production of bumper harvests.

The Hydroponic Technique. Hydroponic crops, under ordinary conditions, are grown in beds of aggregate, usually mixtures of sand and stones, which are periodically moistened by infusion of nutrient solutions. These troughs are kept constantly moist, and the plants are given maximum nourishment in order to encourage higher yields. The operation of the whole system can be made automatic, while the grower, by varying the formula, may produce whatever type of plant is required. Complete control over the crop is achieved. Several modifications of hydroponics exist, and one method makes it possible for the operator to use only a liquid solution without any aggregate. Under this system, the plants are suspended on trays over a tank of water and nutrients, but first-class aeration in a very dry outdoor climate is essential to success. In practice, especially in closed devices like tubes or greenhouses, hydroponic cultures are best if run on the aggregate method, and on the moon this would be doubly true, since it might be considered desirable to increase the supply of carbon dioxide in an effort to raise yield, and that in itself would cut down the amount of oxygen available for the roots, thus diminishing aeration.

A Lunar Farm. Assuming therefore that aggregate culture would be superior, we may envisage as follows a food producing unit on the moon:

The "farm" would consist of a series of transparent tubes, made from toughened plastic material, with one side flattened so as to rest evenly on the lunar surface. This flattened side would act as the base of the hydroponicum that would be set up inside the tube. A diameter of at least 12 feet would be desirable, so as to give height for tall plants, and to allow for two troughs separated by a center walk running down the middle of the unit. The length could be unlimited, but one end would open into a central assembly area where fertilizers, laboratories, and workers' quarters would be situated. In practice, a unit might resemble a wheel, with the tubes radiating off from the central assembly and controlling point or hub. The object of having a number of separate tubes is to enable different types of crops at various stages of growth to be raised at one and the same time. In individual production sections, it would be possible to provide each class of plants with optimum growth conditions.

The troughs or beds inside the tubes would run parallel to the length of the unit. They would be fitted with side walls 8 inches in height, and be about a yard wide, thus allowing for a central passageway of similar breadth. The space just above the top of the rear wall, where the tube bulges outward would provide room for the irrigation pipes, heating cable, and air-conditioning apparatus. Sliding screens to exclude excessive light and electric light bulbs to give illumination during the long nights would also be included in the equipment. The growing troughs themselves would be filled with crushed rock, of $5/8$- to $1/4$-inch grade, which would serve as a support for the roots of the plants, while retaining nutrients and moisture.

At regular intervals, correctly balanced mixtures of chemical fertilizers, or synthetic resins having anion and cation exchange properties, would be applied to the growing crops by even distribution over the surface of the aggregate in the beds, or else by insertion before planting. All these operations can be easily mechanized.

In the absence of insect pests, and the probable total exclusion of soil-borne terrestrial diseases, the use of fungicides or other sprays would be unnecessary. Normal staking and tieing would no doubt be required.

The operation of the hydroponic units could be made completely automatic, and the perfect growing conditions that would be obtained inside the closed tubes of the farm could indeed be a horticulturist's paradise.

No Insurmountable Obstacles. From the above short discussion, it will be already apparent that there are no insurmountable obstacles, at any rate as far as the theoretical aspect is concerned, blocking the way to the establishment of food producing units on the moon. In practice, however, a few technical problems are likely to arise. These are of sufficient importance to justify brief mention.

(a) *Light*. We have found that plants growing under lunar conditions would be provided with light from natural sources. The long period of daily illumination could be exhausting to terrestrial-type plants, which are conditioned to short phase illumination followed by dark periods. It would no doubt be desirable to have screens that might be drawn inside the growing units to shut out light at intervals. In the same way, to secure healthy growth and development during the lunar night, artificial lighting would be essential. Few higher plants could stand perpetual darkness for a fortnight, since during that time chlorophyll formation would be halted, and in consequence general debility followed by necrosis would ensue.

(b) *Heat*. The absence of any dense atmosphere on the moon, which has an albedo of only 7 per cent, means that most of the sun's heat is absorbed. Actually, this merely results in a rise in temperature on the surface until the heat absorbed is balanced by reradiation. No heat penetrates into the surface to any marked degree, although over geological periods the amount might be appreciable. The provision of tubes or domes for the protection of crops would of course enable adequate heating or cooling arrangements to be installed, and there should be little difficulty in insuring that suitable temperatures of from 65° F. to 80° F. were maintained within the farm units. For screening the plants against excessive solar heat during the lunar day, insulation of the units would be required; while at night some warming of the domes would be called for. If root temperatures were allowed to exceed 90° F., excessive transpiration would occur, and the plants would become desiccated.

(c) *Air*. Inside the hydroponic units, an atmosphere similar to the terrestrial air ocean, in composition, would have to be maintained. For different crops, water vapor content could be varied, and these humidity adjustments might prove most valuable in controlling growth. Experiments have been undertaken in commercial greenhouses on earth with the object of ascertaining if any increase in the supply of carbon dioxide results in better growth. No striking improvements have yet been obtained, but it has been found that plants can use more carbon dioxide at high light intensities. This in turn could have appreciable effects on development. Under lunar conditions, it might well be that the supply of the gas in the farms could be increased. No doubt it would be practicable to allow for about 2 per cent CO_2 in the air mixture, against only the 0.03 per cent usual on the earth. The concentration limit for carbon dioxide supply to green plants is 15 per cent. At that level inhibiting growth effects become noticeable.

Gravity. This is another factor that might well become significant. The moon has a low gravity force—less than one sixth of that of the earth. On this planet, plant shoots are negatively geotropic, and roots are positively geotropic. Growth under terrestrial conditions proceeds at certain rates, and the rise of sap and consequent ultimate size of the crop—whether it consists of trees or small annuals—depend to a considerable extent on the influence of gravitational attraction. It is reasonable to assume that under the lower gravity conditions on the moon, green plants would be able to grow far more quickly, and possibly attain greater heights than on earth.

Materials Available on the Moon. Mention has already been made of the possibilities of obtaining supplies of water, nutrients, and aggregate for hydroponic farms on the moon from local sources. With regard to the former, should frozen ice exist in deep crevices in the crust, its conversion into water would be relatively simple. The release of oxygen from the rocks into which it has entered into combination with various minerals should prove quite practicable, and most of the plans for lunar colonization are based on the assumption that large quantities of both air and water would be manufactured by release from the local rocks. These formations could be crushed up for use as building materials and for growing media. No great technical problems would require solution as far as such operations as these were concerned.

The only other point of importance awaiting elucidation would then be the provision of fertilizer chemicals. It would be quite uneconomic to convey chemicals in bulk by spaceship to the moon, and apart from a small initial supply, the lunar hydroponicist would have to rely on local products. The essential elements needed by the green plant have already been reviewed, and it is reasonable to assume that the rocks on the moon would be able to yield appreciable amounts of minerals quite similar to those known on earth. The actual choice of the individual salts which act as vehicles carrying the particular elements for feeding to the plants is immaterial, provided toxic substances are avoided, and correct antagonism and balance are maintained. In practice, compounds like nitrate of soda, sulphate of ammonia, potassium sulphate or muriate, and superphospate of lime are used. Many new combined salts are today coming onto the market, which contain two or three nutrient elements, and considerably reduce the bulk of formulae.

Apart from the cultivation of higher plants and algae on the surface of the moon, good possibilities might exist of establishing mushroom farms in underground caverns. The soilless growing of fungi has not yet been seriously attempted on a practical scale, and several technical problems would arise, such as control of the sugar solutions, but none of these questions would be insoluble. The food value of the edible fungi is high, and they could be produced all through the lunar night at low cost in the absence of light.

Conclusion. From this necessarily brief general outline of the possibilities of establishing food producing units on the moon, the reader will be able to form some idea of the types of farms that are envisaged. No technical details or complete descriptions of apparatus have been given, since the object of this article is simply to bring to the notice of lunar explorers and other interested parties the main problems that might arise, and how they could be overcome.

For various reasons, it is considered that hydroponics, or soilless cultivation, would be the only practicable technique suitable under lunar conditions. The production of higher plants, fungi and algae, should be quite possible, provided protective apparatus of the right design was installed, while it seems reasonable to assume that local supplies of water and nutrients, as well as air and aggregate would be available.

The hydroponic farms that will eventually be developed on the moon would afford absolutely perfect growing conditions, and give the operator complete control over the plants. Crops of greatly superior quality could therefore be raised. Certain modifications in plant characteristics would undoubtedly take place, due to the changed environment, and might perhaps result in crops of giant size, coming to maturity in as little as two weeks.

Handicapped as we are by having not yet had any actual physical contact with the moon, and being comparatively ignorant of what ecological conditions might eventually be produced there, the conclusions reached at present can be only tentative and theoretical. However, hydroponics on the earth is a tested and successful system that has been profitably operated in all sorts of climatic conditions. Given certain essentials, the hydroponicist can today produce crops in any area, independently of the soil, and without relying on nature's whims. There is no doubt that provided these same essentials can be artificially obtained on the moon, crop growing there would also be possible.

Many problems would of course arise, and skill would be needed to solve them. After the establishment of hydroponic units growing plants raised from seed brought from the earth, and the assurance of a regular supply of food from these, the next task of interest for botanists and horticulturists would be the solution of the question of whether any lower types of vegetation do actually flourish on the moon's surface. Various opinions have been put forward about this, some for and some against the possibility of plant life existing under lunar conditions. Only local surveys can give the final answer, but it may well be that certain lower forms of vegetation do grow on crater floors. Whether such plants would be palatable, let alone edible for human beings, is another matter.

* Building on the Moon

After we finally succeed in landing on the moon, the next big problem confronting us will be the construction of a permanent building to serve as living quarters for the crew, as well as providing compartments for offices, laboratories, and whatever other functions may be carried on. As far as possible, everything essential to the life of the community should be housed within one building, as travel from buildng to building in the open would necessitate putting on a space suit, and could be hazardous due to meteoritic bombardment. Owing to the peculiar conditions prevailing on the moon, this building will differ considerably in design from buildings erected for a similar purpose on the earth. Fortunately we have an accurate knowledge of most conditions on the moon and can allow for them in advance. But there are other factors which are still in considerable doubt.

Until recently we have assumed without question that the dark maria which make up the face of the man in the moon are just what they appear to be: smooth solid areas probably due to vast lava sheets. But as we have seen in the article by T. Gold, this concept of the maria is by no means certain. Instead of lava sheets, Gold believes that the maria are great dust basins. Now, dust on the moon is nothing new; astronomers have always been willing to admit a thin dust layer due to the pulverization of meteorites. Gold, however, postulates a dust layer of several thousand feet in depth. It is hard for many selenographers to believe that the maria which look so firm and solid may be as unstable as quicksand. Yet there is observational evidence derived from the rate of cooling of the lunar surface during an eclipse that strongly supports such an idea. Dust is not the most stable material on which to build.

If all the buildings on the moon need to be protected by a meteoritic shield it is hard to see how we are going to grow vegetables by hydroponic farming, as described in the preceding article. During the lunar day of two weeks the plants were to be exposed intermittently to direct sunlight. During the two weeks night they were to be exposed to artificial light. If it turns out that a meteoritic shield is an absolutely indispensable cover for any building however, it may be necessary to resort to artificial light entirely.

Perhaps we are worrying prematurely about the construction of buildings on the moon. Instead of speculating about the difficulties that may lie ahead of us we can simply sit back and wait until we find out for sure. Should we find meteorites raining down on the surface and the maria covered by a fluffy dust layer, we will know that life on the moon is going to be a tough proposition. On the other hand, should we find firm ground underfoot and if the danger from meteorites turns out to be nothing but a myth, our task will be much easier.

*

Basic Design for Moon Building

JOHN S. RINEHART

INTRODUCTION. Man will, within the foreseeable future, construct permanent buildings on the moon to serve as living quarters for moon explorers, laboratories for astrophysical and astrochemical research, maintenance shops for the vehicles of the space traveler, stations for communications networks, and numerous other structures required for many of the common activities of man. How are these buildings to be built? What are the basic design criteria? How do they differ from those applicable to earth-situated buildings? What special facilities must be provided not needed on earth? What are the environmental differences and hazards? What determines the material we use? What problems must the architect and the construction engineer face? How are the materials to be transported?

On the surface of the moon every object will weigh only one sixth as much as on the surface of the earth. The mass or inertia of each object is, however, independent of its location. *In design, one must continually keep the distinction between mass and weight clearly in mind.*

Environmental Conditions. The environment of a building on the moon differs markedly from its environment on the earth. The moon has no observable atmosphere. There is no haze, no clouds, no winds, no rain or snowstorms. The building is either bathed in intense sunshine or looks upon stark, black, cold space. It will be continuously plagued by the great gnatlike rain of interplanetary dust.

The moon has lost its atmosphere, if it ever had any, because of its small size and, hence, low gravitational pull. Thus the atmospheric pressure is zero and

John S. Rinehart, from *Journal of the British Interplanetary Society,* September-October, 1959.

any building constructed there must be internally pressurized with an atmosphere in which humans can survive.

The moon's surface, unshielded by an absorbing atmosphere, can feel the full force of the sun's rays and become extremely hot on one side while the other side will quickly have radiated its heat into space and become exceedingly cold. Day and night are each about two weeks long.

The temperatures on the surface of the moon have been carefully measured, using a telescope equipped with a vacuum thermocouple. It was found that the surface of the moon cools very quickly during an eclipse, reaching minimum temperature in twenty or thirty minutes after the sun stops shining. The temperature at lunar midday is 214° F. (101° C.), at sunset 32° F. (0° C.), and at midnight −243° F. (−153° C.). Curves showing the eclipse measurements and the temperature distribution at full moon [make] it possible to estimate the sort of temperature environment, maximum and minimum temperatures, and rates of changes in temperature any structure placed on the moon will be subjected to. Any structure placed there must be able to withstand these extreme temperatures and especially the tremendous temperature gradients which will abound.

The ultraviolet radiation, normally absorbed by the earth's atmosphere, will be sufficiently intense to render panes of glass or plastic useless as windows through discoloration. Hence, shutters must be provided for such windows.

The moon is continually bombarded by particulate matter: cosmic rays, charged particles, and meteoric particles. Not much is known about the rate of influx of cosmic rays, although recent records from the satellite Explorer III indicate that they are considerably more abundant than we have thought. They probably do not present a health hazard but they may be sufficiently abundant to discolor glass or plastic after long exposure.

Also, it is not possible to define very accurately the nature and distribution of meteoric matter so as to estimate it as a potential hazard to structure. According to Whipple, extraterrestrial material exists in three forms: (1) *interplanetary dust* (the most abundant), ranging in size from 1 to 300 microns in diameter; (2) *meteors*—fragile, porous bodies of low gross density; and (3) *meteorites*—solid chunks of iron and stone. The velocity with which any of this material might strike the moon ranges from 1.5 to 44 miles/sec. There will be no atmosphere to check its velocity, as is the case with the earth, where the interplanetary dust and the meteors are rendered impotent.

The fall of a meteorite is a relatively rare event: about five per day reach the earth. Interplanetary dust is by far more abundant in space, with the abundance of this dust in the vicinity of the moon being about 5×10^{-21} gm/cm³. The moon sweeps up this material at the rate of 110 tons per day.

Thus the chance of a large building being struck by a meteorite or a meteor is negligible, one hit in perhaps several thousand years. Interplanetary dust is the real hazard and we do not know how great it is. The particles are small, and, even though of great velocity, could be easily warded off with an umbrella-like shield. Our best estimate is that about three or four particles with diameters ranging from 0.0002 to 0.0004 inches would strike each square yard of exposed surface per day. *A meteoric shield must be a part of any structure built on the moon* [Plate XVI].

From a practical viewpoint, the exact nature of the surface of the moon is our greatest unknown. On a grand scale we know that the moon's surface is fraught with large and deep craters, mountain ranges, and great flat areas. But we cannot look at the moon in the intimate detail needed to provide us with realistic design data for construction. Resolution with our best telescopes is some hundreds of yards.

Opinion is now divided as to the nature of the moon's landscape. At a United States Air Force symposium on this subject in April, 1958, three eminent astronomers summarized their variant ideas:

(1) "The maria (large dark flat areas) are almost certainly covered with lava and will make firm landing spots for earth's spaceships."

(2) "The rock has turned slowly to dust by bombardment of rays and particles from the sun and space. The dust, kept stirred up by the same agents that formed it, has flowed like a slow liquid into the moon's low places so the maria are not filled with lava, but with dust perhaps several miles deep. Dust near the surface may be as fluffy as baby powder. Unwary ships might disappear in dry quicksand."

(3) "Although the moon may have plenty of dust, its surface has been solidified. There may be a thin layer like dust on a grand piano but underlying material, cemented together (not stirred up) by bombardment from space, is probably 'crunchy' and strong enough to support our alighting spaceships."

With this lack of knowledge and great divergence of opinion we can only design for the worst condition: a sea of dust upon which we must float our structures.

Basic Design Criteria. Without defining the specific function of the building we know that it must provide for the following:

(1) Living quarters, including rooms for sleeping, cooking, eating, and recreation.

(2) Physics, chemistry, and biological laboratories.

(3) A control tower for communication, meteorological studies, earth observations, astronomical observations, traffic control, etc.

(4) Air conditioning, heating, power and refrigeration plants, oxygen production units, extreme-temperature regulating devices, water supply, and sewage disposal plants.

(5) A machine shop and equipment maintenance area. Further, we know that the structure must be built as an integral floatable unit.

We assume the following: (1) that the location of the buliding on the moon will be fixed; (2) that the building will be constructed from materials brought from the earth (this restriction implies at once that no single piece can be heavier than the load-carrying capacity of the cargo space of our future moon rockets) ; (3) that the building will provide the functions listed above; and (4) that it will be a permanent-type building in the sense that it will be occupied on a continuing basis over several years' time.

A moon building presents its own peculiar problems and first is the matter of gravity. The force of gravity on the moon is approximately one sixth that on the earth. This means that the deflection of a cantilever beam or any other load-supporting beam or column will be only one sixth as great as it would be on earth. Changes in gravity will not affect the strength properties of the materials. For design purposes we can, in all static situations (n.b., only static, not dynamic) replace the "g" of 32 ft/sec² which repeatedly appears in our strength of materials formulae by one sixth its value, say 5 ft/sec². A whole new field of design is opened up. It is as if we had an exceedingly high-strength, lightweight construction material.

We must, however, be wary of any dynamic situation. We do not change the mass of our material by transporting it to the moon. It would be just as difficult to accelerate a car on the moon as it is on the earth. Thus, designs involving vibratory or rotary motion must conform to the normal terrestrial pattern. An electric generator designed for lunar use would not appear substantially different from a terrestrial one.

Reduction in gravity will influence the convective flow of air and the rate of flow of liquids downhill. These changes are likely to become important in design of the heating, power, water, sewage, and ventilating systems.

Ramps and stairs can be much steeper because man will be able to lift himself with one sixth the effort required on earth. A crane designed for a 1-ton load on the earth can lift at least 6 tons on the moon. We must, on the other hand, be careful with our elevators for here we are *accelerating* and *decelerating* masses.

No consideration need be given to wind or snow loads since they will not exist. Our major stresses now come from the artificial atmosphere contained within the hermetically sealed building. Normal atmospheric pressure, 14.7 lb/ in², is a realistic figure to use for design purposes; 10 lb/in² would be sufficient. The problem is not unlike that encountered by the designers of high-flying aircraft except perhaps in one respect, which could be significant. On the moon we can play the gravitational forces against the air pressure forces, achieving some kind of equilibrium which may gain us an advantage. This is a matter that needs looking into. Broad expanses of curved structures can be used but we must tie the whole together with rods or similar means so that it does not suffer an internal explosion.

Rapid, intense heating and sudden, severe cooling present difficult, but certainly solvable, design problems. The parts of the structure becoming shaded will immediately become exceedingly cold, while those in the sunlight will remain heated to a high temperature. During the lunar day, when the sun shines upon the structure, devices must be provided to regulate the influx and efflux of heat. These should be tied together to the heating and ventilating systems. But we must also be prepared to be without our principal energy source, the sun, for two weeks at a time. This means providing energy storage facilities of no mean proportion.

The potential hazard from cosmic rays, while still one of the big unknowns, is probably not great enough to warrant modifying constructional practices. Eventually the living quarters may be lined with thin sheets of lead.

The bombardment by meteoric matter is serious, but can be dealt with. The best approach is to use the scheme long in use by tent dwellers to protect themselves from the fury of rainstorms: a canvas canopy covering, placed above and separated some distance from the roof of the tent, which dulls the force of the impact of the raindrops and diverts the material away from the roof of the tent. On the moon, the canopy must be of metal, not canvas, whose thickness will be sufficient to stop meteoritic dust. An aluminum shield 1/32 inch thick should be sufficient. We cannot hope to protect against chance encounters with large meteoric bodies any more than a canvas shield protects against large hailstones. Provision should be made for replacing sections of the shield as they become damaged.

Finally, we are concerned with foundations for the building and here is the greatest difficulty. There seems to be but little else to do but to design the building as a structure which floats in a stationary ocean of dust, anchored in place by large, heavy blocks suspended by long cables from the body of the structure. In many ways its construction will resemble that of a ship at anchor, a freely floating, self-contained unit. The building need not be streamlined. Fortunately, also, it need not be built to withstand the tumultuous forces exerted by a watery ocean. The dust on the moon is as calm as a mill pond.

According to Archimedes' principle, a body immersed in a fluid is buoyed up by a force equal to the weight of the fluid it displaces. A 10,000-ton ship for example, has 320,000 ft³ (1 ft³ of water has a mass of 62.4 lb.) immersed when it is floating. Now, how will our dust ocean act in this respect? We are safe in concluding that it will act as a fluid of low density: for design purposes, about 0.5 times the density of water or 30 lb/ft³. Thus the lower part of our building will be covered with dust, the volume, V, so covered being given by

$$V \text{ (ft}^3) = \frac{Total\ mass\ of\ building\ (lb)}{30}$$

The dust will tend to support the lower floor, or hull. At a depth of 60 feet, the pressure acting on the floor will be just equal to atmospheric pressure. If the hull is embedded to depths greater than this it must be designed so as not to be crushed by the weight of the dust.

Since the building is floating, weight must be fairly uniformly distributed if it is not to topple over or settle in unevenly.

If the moon's surface proves to be sufficiently solid it will provide normal support for the building and may be used as foundation blocks.

The Design. There is no one building uniquely qualified for placement on the moon. Design requirements allow as well as demand a diversity of structural types, proportions, materials, and forms. The portable and inflatable plastic balloon house is a perfectly practical type of temporary housing.

Permanent housing must be fabricated from more durable materials. Aluminum suggests itself immediately because of its high strength, low weight, and ease of fabrication. Aluminum also provides a good reflecting surface which aids in cooling problems.

The basic scientific information needed to complete first designs of functional and attractive buildings for use on the moon are at hand. Our task has been the very specific one of taking these scientific guide lines and producing a practical model.

* What Will We Learn from
—the Moon?

There are two ways of describing conditions on the moon. One is to tell about them in the formal academic textbook style. This does not make for such easy reading, but it does get the facts down in order. The other is to talk about the moon as if you expected to live there sometime. In my book *Exploring Mars,* I decided to adopt the latter method, writing about the moon from the standpoint of the problems involved in establishing an observatory there, as part of a purported 600-page report by the Lunar Planning Commission. This report was signed by the Secretary, a gentleman by the same of Niemand, which also happens to be a German word signifying "nothing" or "nobody."

What will we learn on the moon? The firsthand study of the various lunar formations should tell us something about their origin and possibly throw light on the evolution of the earth-moon system. Since it is very unlikely that there has ever been life on the moon there is little chance of learning anything new in this respect. For this reason, the exploration of the moon will not be nearly so interesting as that of Mars, where the prospect of finding plant life would appear to be rather good. Yet there will be considerable satisfaction in finally settling the nature of the lunar craters and maria, questions which vex us so badly now.

The main reason for going to the tremendous effort of occupying the moon is not that we are particularly concerned about the moon itself, but to use it as a site for observing the sun and stars, and as a jumping-off place for the further exploration of the solar system. In fact, we should consider ourselves very fortunate that we have such a large, conveniently located satellite at our disposal. Certainly the conquest of space should proceed much more smoothly because of our moon. And as for Mr. Niemand's suggestion for naming the craters on the far side, it looks as if the Russians have already jumped in and grabbed off the best sites [Plate XIc].

*

Astronomical Observations from the Moon

ROBERT S. RICHARDSON

AN EXPEDITION dispatched to the moon has returned with such an enthusiastic account of the scientific possibilities of our satellite that a clamor has been made that funds be appropriated immediately for a lunar observatory. Some of the more conservative members of the Interplanetary Planning Commision, however, feel that the conditions under which the instruments would be operated should receive careful consideration before any discussion relating to funds arises. Thereupon, an exhaustive report on lunar surface conditions has been drawn up by the Secretary of the expedition, covering some 600 pages of fine print. Only the condensed twelve-page abstract of the report is given here, which is all that the members of the Interplanetary Planning Commission ever got around to reading anyhow.

Abstract Report on Lunar Surface Conditions. The main purpose in establishing a lunar observatory would be to take advantage of the black sky and perfect seeing conditions that always prevail upon the surface of our satellite, owing to the absence of an atmosphere. The atmosphere of the earth is perpetually disturbed by air currents, which cause twinkling and produce what astronomers call the "seeing." Even on the calmest nights the image of a star or planet as seen through a telescope appears to waver and tremble like that of objects viewed through running water. The space-penetrating power of a telescope is also seriously limited by the sky fog which, even though no artificial lights are near, begins to show on a photographic plate after being exposed for only a few minutes. The sky fog appears to originate from scattered starlight, from the aurora and zodiacal light, and from the glow emitted by atoms and molecules of the air itself. All these, except the zodiacal light, would be completely eliminated by taking astronomical observations from the moon.

Furthermore, we would receive *all* the light of the stars instead of only about 70 per cent, the amount that can penetrate our atmosphere to the surface of the earth. The worst part about the atmosphere from a strictly astronomical

Robert S. Richardson, from *Exploring Mars*, McGraw-Hill, New York, 1954, pp. 53-65.

standpoint is that it blots out the ultraviolet light of the sun and stars, which, although invisible to our eyes, can be readily photographed. The ultraviolet light of the heavenly bodies would, if we could only observe it, give us valuable information about their constitution. Thus even a small telescope on the moon would give us information that we can never hope to obtain with the largest telescope on earth.

From the moon, the disk of the sun would appear nearly white, while the rose-colored prominences at its edge would be always visible, together with the long, pearly streamers of the corona. Stars would be visible even in broad daylight as hard, unwinking points of light, although the glare from the landscape would be so blinding that only the brightest could be discerned. But during the lunar night of approximately fourteen days, so many stars would be visible that it would be hard to trace the outline of even the most familiar constellations.

The Secretary's abstract continues:

The observatory would, of course, have to be in constant communication with the earth. There should be no difficulty on this score, provided that the signals are always broadcast on a frequency high enough to pierce the electrified layers of the earth's upper atmosphere, called the ionosphere. It is well established that this frequency varies widely with the sunspot cycle of eleven years. Thus, when sunspots are scarce, at sunspot minimum, radio waves with a frequency of 6,500 kilocycles will pierce the ionosphere. But at sunspot maximum, the signals will be reflected back into space unless the frequency is above 12,000 kilocycles.

Terrestrial observatories are generally situated on a plateau or mountain peak, often far from a large city, so that electrical power has to be either generated on the spot or transmitted over long distances. On the moon, we are fortunate that we can take advantage of the vast supply of energy that is ours for the asking. For two weeks the sun shines steadily in a sky unstained by haze or clouds. This power can be utilized to operate the telescope, the laboratories, and machine shops, besides supplying the astronomers with oxygen and water derived from mineral sources.

During the lunar day at a point directly beneath the sun the temperature of the surface is about 212° F., or about the boiling point of water. When the sun is just above the horizon, the temperature of the surface is about −58° F., and during the long lunar night the temperature falls as low as −243° F. Such an extreme range between day and night would make it advisable to have the living quarters and other facilities underground at controlled conditions, so far as is feasible.

One of the most serious threats to the lunar observatory (or any structure exposed above ground, for that matter) is the ever-present danger from meteoric bombardment. Meteorites rarely reach the surface of the earth, since they are vaporized by friction in the upper atmosphere. But on the moon, without this protecting shield, these particles could pelt the surface wth velocities up to 44 miles per second.

We have as yet been unable to make accurate counts of the rate of incidence of meteorites upon the lunar surface per day of twenty-four hours. Preliminary estimates put the number conservatively at a million. On this basis the probability that a meteorite would strike a surface equal in extent to the area of a 100-inch mirror is roughly 1/2,000,000. The vast majority of these meteorites are tiny particles no larger than a grain of sand. Although these figures sound reassuring some of us have the uneasy feeling that the danger from meteoritic bombardment should not be so lightly dismissed as in the writings of certain authors, who discuss this peril while securely ensconced in their luxurious offices on the earth. At the worst, however, the danger of being hit by a meteorite on the moon is probably less than that of being run over or shot on the earth.

The report then considered certain problems which would arise in establishing a lunar observatory:

We scarcely need remind members of the committee that a telescope must, to follow the stars in their daily motion across the sky, have one axis mounted parallel to the axis of the planet's rotation. Thus in the Northern Hemisphere of the earth, the polar axis of a telescope is always directed toward an imaginary point in the sky called the north celestial pole, which happens at present to be within one degree of a star of the second magnitude named Polaris.

The same situation, of course, holds true on the moon. For a telescope in the northern hemisphere of the moon to follow the stars, the polar axis must be accurately directed toward the north celestial pole of the lunar heavens. This point happens to fall near a faint star named 36 Draconis, which, for want of a better, will have to serve as the polaris of the moon.

Telescopes on the earth are geared to turn at the rate of 360° in 23 hours 56 minutes 4 seconds, the period of rotation relative to the stars. The moon rotates much more slowly, requiring 27.3 days (more accurately, 27.321661 days) to make a complete rotation with respect to the stars. A lunar telescope will perforce, therefore, run much more slowly than one based upon the earth. There is no trouble, of course, in making a telescope move at whatever rate we please, but on the moon another effect arises, which introduces complications not encountered in the mounting of terrestrial instruments.

We said that "at present" the north celestial pole of the earth is within one degree of the star Polaris. The orientation of the earth's axis in space is not fixed, but describes a circle similar to the conical motion of a spinning top. This circle, as traced in the sky, has a radius of 23½°, with its center in the constellation of Draco. The north celestial pole rotates around this circle once every 26,000 years. Let a member of the committee imagine that he is outdoors facing toward the north and that this circle is marked on the sky in luminous paint.

Imagine further that time is enormously speeded, so that a century passes in the space of a single second. A bright spot representing the north celestial pole would then appear to be moving away from Polaris in a direction contrary to the hands of a clock. After 5,600 years it would pass near the star Alpha Cephei and, 7,000 years later, near the bright star Vega. But after it leaves Vega, another 12,000 years would have to pass before the pole would return to Polaris.

The moon's axis of rotation is also describing a circle in space, but instead of having a radius of $23\frac{1}{2}°$ like that of the earth, it has one of only $1\frac{1}{2}°$. But its motion is much faster. Instead of 26,000 years, it makes a revolution in $18\frac{1}{2}$ years. This motion is too fast to be ignored, as upon the earth. Now our tentative plans call for a lunar telescope built on the same scale as the 100-inch telescope on Mount Wilson. At the principal focus of the 100-inch mirror, $1/10°$ corresponds to 1 inch on the photographic plate. On this scale a photograph of the moon taken at the principal focus of the Mount Wilson telescope would be 10 inches in diameter.

What would happen if we took a photograph of the stars with our telescope on the moon? The axis of rotation of the moon is shifting westward at the rate of 1 degree every nineteen days. Since the telescope is rigidly attached to the moon, it will shift along with it. The result would be that after an exposure of forty-eight hours the star images, instead of being *points* on the plate, would be drawn out into lines an inch long, like the streaks left by stars on the photograph of a comet. The engineering staff will undoubtedly have a fascinating problem to face in designing a special drive to compensate for this conical motion of the lunar axis.

Lunar time was also discussed by the Secretary:

Another important piece of equipment is an accurate timepiece. Many observatories still depend for time upon the operation of a pendulum-driven clock. Rumors have come to us from apparently reliable sources that certain economy-minded members of the Interplanetary Planning Commission hope to save the taxpayers a few dollars by having some of these old pendulum clocks transferred to the lunar observatory. In this connection we would like to point out that the period of a pendulum swing depends not only upon its length but also upon the acceleration of gravity at the station. If a pendulum 39 inches long is set in motion upon the earth, the time of one swing will be approximately 1 second. The pendulum is so sensitive to gravity that the exact length has to be determined by trial and error at each station.

It should therefore be obvious that the best pendulum clock in the world will not keep time on the moon, where the force of gravity is one sixth of that upon the earth. The pendulum, instead of making one swing per second, would now require 2.5 seconds. To keep time as we measure it upon the earth, the length of the pendulum would have to be reduced to 6.5 inches. We would prefer not to use pendulum clocks at all but rather some timepiece controlled by the vibrations of a quartz crystal, vibrations which are independent of gravity.

Several members of the committee have made inquiries regarding the general appearance of the landscape as viewed from the moon. Since the difference in direction between the axis of the earth and moon is only about 23°, we would see mostly the same familiar constellations from the northern hemisphere of the moon as are visible from the United States and Europe. These constellations rise in the east and set in the west, but, as we have already noted, at a much slower pace than on the earth. The sun moves even more deliberately than the stars— always almost exactly due east—and takes nearly fifteen days to pass across the sky and set in the west. The sun does not move to the north and south appreciably, so there are no seasons on the moon.

From our temporary station near the lunar equator, the earth looms overhead as a bluish globe four times the size of the moon as it appears in the earth's sky. To the casual observer it seems to hang as if fixed in the sky, but upon closer examination it is found to swing back and forth about four times its width to the east and west during the month, and about three times its width to the north and south. Although the earth seems nearly motionless relative to the landscape, a few hours' observation is enough to show that it is moving fairly rapidly with respect to the stars, passing over an apparent distance equal to its width in about four hours. This motion of the earth is, of course, really due to the revolution of the moon around it.

When the moon is "new," and therefore visible from the earth as a thin crescent, the earth is nearly "full" as seen from the moon and illuminates the night surface with a bluish light 50 to 60 times brighter than moonlight.

In closing, we wish to emphasize that in our opinion, the expenditure of a few billion dollars would be a trifling sum to pay for the flood of new scientific knowledge of incalculable value that would accrue almost immediately from the establishment of a lunar observatory like that described in detail in the main body of the report. Members of the committee might also be interested to know that in a reconnoitering flight over the side of the moon always turned away from the earth, we noted dozens of fine craters, many exceeding Tycho and Copernicus in size and splendor. On the earthward side of the moon, all the good craters already bear the names of noted scientists, philosophers, and patrons of science. Now, since time immemorial, astronomers have had the exclusive privilege of assigning names to the various lunar formations (see the memoir by the British Astronomical Association entitled *Who's Who in the Moon*). It is possible that, if a generous appropriation for a lunar observatory be forthcoming, the members of the Interplanetary Planning Commission might receive favorable consideration when the delicate question of selecting suitable names for the craters of the invisible hemisphere arises.

I have the honor to be,

Very respectfully, your obedient servant,
I. M. Niemand, *Secretary*

Suggestions for Further Reading

BOOKS

Alter, Dinsmore. *Introduction to the Moon.* Los Angeles: Griffith Observatory, 1946, 108 pp. Comments on various lunar formations by an astronomer who has devoted considerable time to their study at the telescope. Illustrated with some fine photographs. Popular.

Alter, Dinsmore, and Cleminshaw, C. H. *Pictorial Astronomy.* Los Angeles: Griffith Observatory, 1943, 296 pp. An explanation of various subjects of interest in astronomy with numerous illustrations and diagrams. Popular.

Baldwin, Ralph B. *The Face of the Moon.* Chicago: University of Chicago Press, 1948, 239 pp. A good historical account of the development of selenology. It is famous for the discussion of the origin of the lunar craters by meteoritic impact. Semipopular.

Clarke, Arthur C. *The Exploration of Space.* New York: Harper & Bros., 1952, 199 pp. An account of the possibilities of the exploration of the moon and Mars and even interstellar planets. Popular.

Duncan, John Charles. *Astronomy.* New York: Harper & Bros., 1955, 500 pp. A textbook with many fine illustrations. Popular.

Kooy, J. M. J., and Uytenbogaart, J. W. H. *Ballistics of the Future.* New York: McGraw-Hill Book Co., 1946, 472 pp. A highly mathematical account of rocket flight.

Kuiper, G. P. (ed.). *The Atmospheres of the Earth and Planets.* Chicago: University of Chicago Press, 1951, 434 pp. A collection of papers by the editor and other experts on the atmospheres of the planets, their constitution, and origin. Technical.

Ley, Willy. *Rockets, Missiles, and Space Travel.* New York: The Viking Press, 1953, 436 pp. Rather out-of-date now but an excellent, detailed account up to its time. Contains many references in foreign languages. Popular.

Neison, Edmund. *The Moon.* London: Longmans, Green and Co., 1876, 576 pp. Out of print now but often available in scientific libraries. Contains maps and detailed descriptions of lunar formations. Semipopular.

Richardson, Robert S. *The Fascinating World of Astronomy.* New York: McGraw-Hill Book Co., 1960, 274 pp. A question and answer book written in conversational style about various subjects of interest in astronomy. Numerous illustrations. Popular.

Seifert, Howard S. (ed.). *Space Technology.* New York: John Wiley and Sons, 1959, 33 chapters (no page numbers). A collection of often highly mathematical articles dealing with space flight and related subjects. Technical.

Skilling, William T., and Richardson, Robert S. *A Brief Text in Astronomy*. New York: Henry Holt and Co., 1958, 353 pp. A condensed account of modern astronomy. Numerous illustrations. Elementary.

Urey, H. C. *The Planets*. New Haven: Yale University Press, 1952, 245 pp. Map of moon in back. A discussion by an authority on the origin and constitution of the terrestrial planets. Semipopular but not easy reading. Some mathematics.

Von Braun, Wernher, Whipple, Fred L., and Ley, Willy. *Conquest of the Moon*. New York: The Viking Press, 1953, 126 pp. Contains full-color illustrations by Chesley Bonestell, Fred Freeman, and Rolf Klep. Popular.

Whipple, Fred L. *Earth, Moon and Planets*. New York: Grosset and Dunlap, 1958, 293 pp. A clear concise account of our knowledge of the planets. Illustrated. Popular.

Wilkins, H. Percy, and Moore, Patrick. *The Moon*. New York: The Macmillan Co., 1959, 388 pp. "A complete description of the surface of the moon, containing the 300-inch Wilkins' lunar map." Semipopular.

PERIODICALS

Astrophysical Journal. University of Chicago Press, Chicago, Ill. Highly technical, mathematical articles mostly on the stars and nebulae but occasionally a paper on the moon and planets.

Griffith Observer. Griffith Observatory, P.O. Box 27787, Los Feliz Station, Los Angeles 27, Calif. A monthly magazine with articles of current astronomical interest. The positions of the stars and planets for the month are given. Popular.

Journal of the British Interplanetary Society and *Spaceflight*. 12, Bessborough Gardens, London, S.W.1. Authoritative articles on space flight and the planets. Some articles are popular while others are highly mathematical.

Monthly Notices of the Royal Astronomical Society. Burlington House, London, W.1. An English publication corresponding to the *Astrophysical Journal* in the United States. Contains mostly highly technical articles about sun, stars, and nebulae, but occasionally some are found on the moon and planets.

Proceedings of the Lunar and Planetary Exploration Colloquiums. A transcription of speeches delivered at meetings of this society. Copies are given free of charge to members invited to attend. Semipopular. For information write to Dr. E. R. van Driest, Aero-Space Laboratories, Missile Division, North American Aviation, Inc., 12214 Lakewood Blvd., Downey, Calif.

Publications of the Astronomical Society of the Pacific. 675 Eighteenth Ave., San Francisco 21, Calif. Semitechnical articles with occasional mathematics written mostly by astronomers on the Pacific coast. Articles are mostly on astrophysics but some are on the moon and planets.

Sky and Telescope. Charles A. Federer, Jr. (ed.). Sky Publishing Corp., Harvard College Observatory, 60 Garden Street, Cambridge 38, Mass. An excellent monthly magazine on subjects of current astronomical interest.

Lantern slides and 8 x 10 photographic prints of the celestial bodies may be obtained from the Bookstore of the California Institute of Technology, 1201 East California St., Pasadena, Calif. Catalogue available.

Index

Robert S. Richardson was born in Kokomo, Indiana, in 1902. After receiving his Ph.D in astronomy from the University of California in Berkeley, he served as a staff member of the Mount Wilson and Palomar Observatories from 1931 to 1958. Since that time he has been Associate Director of the Griffith Observatory in Los Angeles.

An astronomer who has specialized in the study of the sun and the planets, Dr. Richardson is the author of numerous technical and popular articles and seven previous books including both fiction—*Five Against Venus* and *Second Satellite*—and nonfiction—*Exploring Mars* and *The Fascinating World of Astronomy*.

A member of the American Astronomical Society and the British Interplanetary Society, Dr. Richardson makes his home with his wife and daughter in Altadena, California.

Chesley Bonestell was born in San Francisco in 1888. His lifelong interest in astronomy dates from his reading of Laplace's nebular hypothesis at the age of ten, and since that time he has combined his skills as an artist with his knowledge of astronomy. After attending Columbia University's School of Architecture, he worked first as a designer and renderer for some of the leading architects of the time, and then as a special artist on the *Illustrated London News*. Returning to America in 1927 he worked in Hollywood as a sketch artist and on special camera effects.

With this background it is not surprising that Mr. Bonestell is acknowledged to be one of the masters of astronomical illustration. He is known for his forty-foot mural of the moon in the lobby of the Boston Planetarium, and his paintings have illustrated four previous books, including *The Conquest of Space* (by Willy Ley) and *The Exploration of Mars* (by Willy Ley and Wernher von Braun).

Mr. Bonestell lives with his wife in Altadena, California.

Northern Hemisphere of the Moon

(SEE INDEX OVERLEAF)